THE WHEATFIELDS STORY
1854 - 2002
(from Family Home to Care Centre)

BY
RONALD NELSON REDMAN

Published in 2002
by Sue Ryder Care Wheatfields
Grove Road, Headingley, Leeds, LS6 2AE

© Text Copyright: Ronald Nelson Redman

ISBN: 0-9539740-9-X

Designed by Blueprint Marketing Services Limited • Ilkley
Printed by Amadeus Press Ltd, Bradford

Dedication

This book is dedicated to all the Volunteers, past and present, who have given
such love and dedicated effort in support of Wheatfields.

Contents

Introduction 4

Acknowledgements 5

Chapter 1:
Headingley - from a forest clearing to a premier northern suburb of Leeds 7

Chapter 2:
Plot No 23 - The Wheatfield (not a place for a common brewhouse) 11

Chapter 3:
Wheatfield Lodge. No 11 Wood Lane - The ultimate 'gentleman's residence' 15

Chapter 4:
Wheatfield between the wars 28

Chapter 5:
Wheatfield House goes to war! 34

Chapter 6:
Faith, Hope and Charity 41

Chapter 7:
Wheatfields Hospice - The dream becomes reality 58

Chapter 8:
On to the Millennium and beyond 70

INTRODUCTION

You can never fully retire from Wheatfields. Just before I officially retired from the fundraising team, it was suggested I might like to write up the history of the old house. Little did I know that almost four years later, after much research and interviewing I would come up with over 30,000 words on the subject, spanning almost 150 years.

Wheatfield House in formal terms is an 'Italian villa style' built of local sandstone with low pitched slate roofs and with bracketed eaves. Generally of two storeys, but with a three storey tower over the entrance which itself has a porch with free standing Tuscan columns, the exterior is otherwise relatively plain. In contrast, the interior is much embellished, with ornate plasterwork, etc., warranting its status as a Grade II listed building.

It had quite a story to tell even before it became a hospice in 1978. Through the centuries, the word 'hospice' has meant a place for weary travellers to rest and be refreshed. In modern times, 'hospice' represents the special quality of care given to people with life-threatening illnesses, a place where patients and their families can face their journey with comfort and dignity.

As one hospice family member put it: 'It's a place which is all about living. A Hospice helps people to live until it's time for them to die and helps people who have experienced a devastating loss to live again.'

During my research I have spoken to so many interesting people as can be seen in my extensive acknowledgements but, in the end, this text is my own interpretation of the available facts, so any mistakes are entirely my own.

I would welcome hearing from anyone who can shed any more light on the history and in particular any early photographs which could be made available for any future edition. Yes, this is an open ended story - history is being made all the time at the Sue Ryder Care Centre, known to many thousands of grateful people as Wheatfields.

So, journey with me through the history of this fine old house, and see the part it has played in the community for so many years.

Ronald Nelson Redman,
14A, Oliver Hill,
Horsforth,
LEEDS LS18 4JF

ACKNOWLEDGEMENTS

It would be quite impossible to list all the people I have contacted or spoken to in the course of compiling this history, so if I have forgotten anyone I ask their forgiveness.

I must place on record my grateful thanks to the following:
Mr. Claud Nicholson for details of the family history and recollections of childhood days at Wheatfield House. The photographs made available allowed me to record the rebuilding of the house in the 1880s in great detail and his contributions to this history have been enormous.

For the years between the two World Wars:
Mrs. M. Batty, Mrs. M. Gledhill, Mrs. N. Miller, Mr. R. Simpson, Mrs. J.H. Spivey, Dr. J.F. Wilson, Mrs. S. Youell.

For recollections of the Second World War:
Miss M.J. Baildon, Mr. R. Bradley, Mrs. D. Fletcher, Mrs. N. Moody.

Post War recollections:
Mr. L. Birch, Mr. P. Brown, Mrs. M. Gadd,
Mr. S.H. Hanson, Mrs. D. Marshall, Mr. D. Park, Mr. F. Ward.

For the early history of the Hospice:
Dr. D. J. Charley, Rev. P. Clarke, Mr. M. Fray, Mrs. K. Merryweather, Mrs. M. Murphy, Mr. M. Townsend. Staff and Volunteers: Mrs. B. Barrett, Mr. M. Bourne, Mrs. M. Bray, Mrs. O. Finney, Mr. and Mrs. E. Foote, Miss A. Garside, Mrs. G. Pollard, Mrs. P. Riley, Mrs. A. Robinson, Mrs. S. Tatterton, Mrs M. Turner, Mrs. P. Walker, Miss L. Wood.

I have consulted back issues of the Wheatfield 'Link' as well as numerous annual reports, plus three very interesting early scrapbooks compiled by Mrs. Mary Stratton, kindly loaned to me by Alyson Wort. I was made most welcome and assisted by Headingley Library, Headingley Parish Magazine, Leeds City Council Department of Legal Services, Leeds District Archives at Sheepscar, Leeds Reference Library, West Yorkshire Archive Service in Wakefield, The Yorkshire Archaeological Society.

I thank Mr. Peter Thornton for his valuable assistance in explaining legal documents and reducing them to layman's terms. As ever, my appreciation to my wife Jean for her encouragement and for typing countless letters and drafts of text, and for the proof reading done by her with her sister Eileen Appleby, for which I am very grateful.

Last, but by no means least, I place on record my great debt of gratitude to Joan Whittaker, my voluntary secretary during my years at Wheatfields. She is one of only two ladies who can read my writing (who said scribble?), and cope with a conspicuous lack of punctuation. She typed the final draft and is as delighted as I am that I have now completed it!

*The overall front elevation of Wheatfields in its extended form as reproduced by
Hepper and Sons, Leeds sales brochure for October 1919, and aptly captioned "the
superbly appointed residence known as Wheatfield."*

6

CHAPTER 1

HEADINGLEY - FROM A FOREST CLEARING TO A PREMIER NORTHERN SUBURB OF LEEDS

To cricket lovers the world over the very name of Headingley conjures up the home of Yorkshire cricket from 1888, and its famous sloping pitch, the scene of so many exciting test matches, with the scene being described on radio by the unmistakeable voices of John Arlott or Brian Johnston as Fred Trueman runs up to bowl from the Kirkstall Lane End.

Inevitably, the history of this northern suburb and its first inhabitants on the high ground between the Aire and Wharfe valleys goes back some 5000 years to the stone age, following the retreat of the ice age, which made the ridge a possible place to settle. Sadly, the passage of time has eradicated all evidence of the early settlement and many of the signs of the invading forces who tramped through this area - the Romans, the Vikings and the Normans.

A small township was established in what became Adel around 250 B.C., not far from the two small clearings that would, in time, be Headingley. The area was an immense forest of oak trees, in which limited felling of the timber provided material for building crude shelters, and the creating of grazing areas for pigs and limited flocks of sheep and goats.

From about 100 B.C. the whole of the north of England came under the banner of the KINGDOM OF BRIGANTIA, named after the Brigantes, a race of iron age Celtic warriors, where the natural tongue was the old Celtic language, from which the area first acquired a fixed name, HEDDE-INGAS-LEAH, roughly translated as 'the forest clearing of Hedde'. Hedde was probably the name of the elder of the tribe at the time when they were becoming more organised as they faced the arrival of the invading army of the Roman Empire.

During the occupation of the Leeds (LOIDIS) area, the legion had time to display their skills at roadbuilding, when they constructed the first transpennine route, joining York to Lancaster, passing through Adel on its way to Ilkley. During this period the Headingley tribal population became part of the Celtic kingdom of Elmet, who safeguarded their future by remaining allies of Rome until the invaders departed from our shores in the year 410.

Over the space of 200 years the north of Britain eventually fell under the control of the combined forces of the Angles and Saxons, who drew the tiny kingdom of Elmet into the territory of Northumbria. The next foreign invaders came on the scene in 866, when the Vikings arrived to stamp their rule on the area. Contrary to their image, as portrayed in Hollywood film sagas, they introduced their efficient and highly organised form of government, starting with the division of the 'broad acres' into the three ridings, which in turn were sub-divided into local governments or councils called 'Wapentakes'. The Headingley area became the Skyrack Wapentake, this still popular name 'Skyrack' being derived from the word 'Siaraches' or 'Bright Oak', based around the famous shire oak, for many centuries a symbol of the centre of Headingley.

Yet more sweeping changes were inevitable following the next invasion, when William of Normandy landed in the south of England during the year 1066 - a date drilled into the memory of all schoolchildren throughout the years! All revolts against the newcomers from over the channel were crushed within three years, when William chose one of his lords Ilbert De Lacy to become the first Baron of West Yorkshire. Ilbert soon elevated one of his henchmen, Ralf Pagenal, to Lord of the Manor of Leeds and Headingley. Following the poor assessment of the area in the Doomsday Survey of 1086, the Lordship of the Manor of Headingley was entrusted to William Peytvin, a dynasty that remained in the area for the next two centuries.

The catalyst for the great changes over this period was to be the Cistercian Order, the monks of which were named after the Abbey of Citeaux in Burgundy, and within their rigorously controlled monasteries became prolific farmers and monumental builders. In 1152 Abbot Alexander, an ex-prior of Fountains Abbey, gave up his intention to establish a monastery at Barnoldswick and turned to marshy ground on the sheltered banks of the river Aire to site the "Monastery of Hedingley Woods", to become more famous as Kirkstall Abbey. His initial group of 12 Monks and 10 Lay Brothers soon started to drain the land, fell the trees, and break up the fallow ground, as well as erecting the timber and stone monastery, which took 30 years of labour.

Granges, or farming out stations, were created on the cleared areas, giving rise to local names such as 'Moor Grange', still in use to this day. The new grass lands supported flocks of sheep as they introduced the famous 'golden fleece', and its subsequent industry, to West Yorkshire. By 1300 they milled their own as well as neighbours' grain, and surplus leather, pottery and iron goods were made available for resale. The monks had become the first iron masters of Kirkstall, a tradition taken up by the famous Kirkstall Forge, situated half a mile up the valley on the same bank of the Aire.

Apart from the river, another important source of power was Meanwood beck, which started to turn the wheels of a new mill established near Grove Lane by the Lord of the Manor of Headingley in the late 12th century.

Sweeping changes came again to the area following the dissolution of the monasteries by Henry VIII. Abbot William Marshall surrendered Kirkstall Abbey in 1539, and soon the once proud building was reduced to a ruin by the systematic plundering of the Abbey for its stone, glass, timber and lead, resulting in the ruin much as we see it today.

Many of the evicted monks, with their practical experience in the manufacture of woollen cloth, or farming, soon settled in the community. The ruins of the Abbey passed through many hands before being finally purchased and presented to the City of Leeds in 1898 by Colonel John North, a local man who had made millions of pounds on the west coast of South America, where he acquired the soubriquet 'The Nitrate King'.

Elizabeth I presented the Abbey, and its lands, in 1584 to Robert Savile, whose family became the Earls of Sussex, and by marriage, the Earls of Cardigan (family name Brudenell). Leeds street names still record the names of these worthies!

Headingley village would appear to have avoided the vicissitudes of the civil war, despite being on the edge of the Battle of Leeds in nearby Meanwood Valley during January 1643, when the town was lost to the Parliamentarians. Inevitably, the monarchy returned following the Cromwellian period, when Charles II introduced a 1663 government survey to levy a 'Hearth Tax'. The local returns only listed 38 houses, but these included no less than 76 'hearths' for a population of approximately 200 souls. By 1700 most of the area was in the hands of the absentee landlord, the Earl of Cardigan, where it remained for over a century, and even the main road by-passed the village.

The 19th century saw monumental changes as the 1829 Enclosures Act allowed most of what was left of the common moorland to be split into plots by the main local landowners for resale for development. Grazing rights for common land were withdrawn, and the days of the mainly agricultural community were over. The seeds were sown that would, in time, blossom into the premier northern suburb of Leeds.

The boom town of Leeds, a product of the industrial revolution, had mushroomed to embrace over 100 Woollen Mills, providing work for in excess of 10,000 people. Soon public transport was essential, and the area had a first class Stage Coach service, which was reaching its zenith just prior to the coming of the railways. Stage Coaches were, however, only for the rich, the 'Concorde' travel of the day!

The explosion of the population in the first half of the 19th century recorded it soaring from 30,000 to 101,000, and not surprisingly both the air, and eventually the water supply, were polluted. The once attractive inner suburbs and squares soon lost their appeal, and the successful merchants started to move north to the leafy higher ground and the fresh air of Chapel Allerton and Headingley.

Victoria came to the throne in 1837, the start of the 64 year Victorian age when the power of steam provided the muscle for a vigorous nation. Thirty million tons of coal were mined in 1837, rising to two hundred million by 1897 - no wonder there was pollution on a grand scale! In the first year of Victoria's reign, Headingley's population reached 4000, but worthy of note, even at that early date, only approximately half of these worked in the immediate area. The improvement of the road surfaces joining Woodhouse with Headingley Road, later to become Headingley Lane, led to the introduction of the first Horse Bus service between the town centre (the Nags Head) and Far Headingley (the Three Horse Shoes). Five journeys a day each way for a single fare of 6d a sum only practical for the middle class to partake of the service. The road eventually continued through to Otley, to become the Leeds-Otley turnpike (tolls not abolished in Leeds until 1866). Headingley was now well and truly on the map, and even had a station on the Leeds-Harrogate & Thirsk line by 1849, unfortunately rather badly sited on the outskirts of the area.

The agent for the Cardigan estate, with the support of other leading landowners, spent five years completing the survey of 130 acres of Headingley Moor by 1834, enabling Parliament to pass the sale of land, conveniently recorded as "the said common and wasteground yield little profit, and in their present state are incapable of any considerable improvement"!

This description was, of course, far removed from the hyperbole introduced by the property or land agents, who soon 'honed in' on Headingley with announcements aimed at the Nouveau Riche. Typical of these were - "very pleasantly situated about two miles from Leeds in a county remarkable for the respectability of its occupants", or comments like "parochial taxes very trifling", or "area rich in springs and wells", or possibly, best of all, "the beauties of Headingley and its neighbourhood, and the salubrity of the air, are too well known to require any observation".

It was some time before all the plots of land on the Cardigan estate were to change hands, and it was not until the 28th March 1854 that Jacob Wood purchased Plot No. 23, and its original use may be judged by its title - "WHEAT FIELD".

CHAPTER 2
Plot No 23 – THE WHEATFIELD
(NOT A PLACE FOR A COMMON BREWHOUSE)

On the 28th March 1854 Mr. Jacob Wood completed the purchase of part of a close of land in Headingley-cum-Burley in the Parish of Leeds, bounded by the property of James Fox (now the site of St. Michael's C.of E. Primary School). Both gentlemen had secured land from the estates of the Rt. Honorable James Thomas, Earl of Cardigan.

Mr. Wood's plot cost him £338.9s.5d., and 'The Wheatfield' recorded as Plot No. 23 on the sale plan, is described as follows:-

"Containing one half of the road or street on the Northward and Eastward sides thereof, 6140 superficial square yards or thereabouts, more or less, bounded on or towards the North by the centre of the new road or street (Alma Road) No. 4 on the sale plan, 'or towards the East by the centre of the new road or street (Grove Road) or towards the South by a private carriage road and public bridleway and footway (then Oil Mill Lane soon to become Wood Lane,) and on towards the West by land sold by the estates to Mr. James Fox."

Jacob Wood was no stranger to the Earl of Cardigan Estates, as his family had lived and worked at Headingley Mill (at the foot of what became Wood Lane near to Grove Road) on which his father, Thomas Wood, had taken out a lease on the Messuage, oil mills and lands way back in 1824. The Estate Rent Rolls of 1858 record the annual rent at £52.10.0. per annum.

We must assume that Jacob purchased the Wheatfield in order to build a family home of some stature, but this was Headingley, where standards and restrictions were being levelled at proposed developers.

The restrictions were very comprehensive, and are still the same for the site to this very day, and are worthy of recording verbatim:-

"The said Jacob Wood his heirs or assigns shall not erect any building or buildings on the plot or parcel of land which shall be occupied or made use of as or for a DYEHOUSE, SLAUGHTERHOUSE, GLASSHOUSE, GASHOUSE, DISTILLERY or COMMON BREWHOUSE, NOR AS A PLACE FOR MELTING TALLOW, MAKING CANDLES, BOILING SOAP, BURNING BLOOD, BAKING OR REFINING SUGAR OR MAKING GLUE. NOR AS A PLACE WHERE ANY STEAM POWER MIGHT BE REQUIRED FOR ANY PURPOSE WHATSOEVER, NOR AS A WORKING SHOP OR A PLACE FOR A MANUFACTURING CHEMIST, POTTER, BLACKSMITH, WHITESMITH, TANNER, SKINNER OR CURRIER, NOR AS A PLACE WHEREIN ANY OTHER NOISY NOISESOME OFFENSIVE OR DANGEROUS TRADE MIGHT BE CARRIED ON. NOR SHOULD ANY SUCH BUILDING OR BUILDINGS BE USED AS OR FOR A BREWHOUSE SHOP OR FOR THE SALE OF ANY GOODS, WARES OR MERCHANDISE WHATSOEVER."

A detailed search of the West Riding Registry of Deeds in Wakefield revealed that Jacob Wood was becoming quite a land and property speculator taking no less than four tenets of land under his wing during 1854. Sadly, early property is not so well recorded, and no drawings or plans for the first house, known as Wheatfield Lodge can be found. So, neither Jacob, nor his wife Mary Ann, and children, Annie, Elizabeth, Katherine and Thomas Henry, ever lived on the site during their rather short tenure of 'The Wheatfield'.

Jacob Wood died on 3rd December 1858. His Will dated 7th November 1858, duly proved in the District Registry of His Majesty's Court of Probate at Wakefield on 8th January 1859, left all his property, real and personal, to his wife with provision for the education of his children. However, problems arose with regard to 'The Wheatfield', and it seems that Jacob had run into financial difficulties, as at some unrecorded date he had entered into a contract of agreement to sell at a loss 'The Wheatfield' to his neighbour James Fox, a local architect and surveyor, for £300.

The contract was sealed with a modest £30 deposit, but Fox hardly rushed to finalise the purchase, and only paid a further £100 to Wood's Trustees on 13th April 1861 well after Jacob Wood's death.

It was about this time that the sales saga became very complex as James Fox agreed to transfer his contract to a Mr. Isaac Israel sealed with a payment of £130 as the first of three instalments totalling £415, for the Wheatfield site. The transaction was not completed until 11th December 1865 when the first payment of £115 was transferred to James Fox, Mary Ann Wood and her late husband's Trustees.

We must assume the building of the first house named Wheatfield Lodge must have commenced in 1859, as the April 1861 Census for Headingley-cum-Burley reveals the residents as follows: Isaac Israel (Naturalised German) aged 34, his wife Matilda (born London) aged 28, and daughter Frances (born Headingley) aged 10. Three general servants are also listed: Elizabeth Nelson aged 25 from Greetland, Mary Ganneil aged 25 from Oulton, and Louisa Wilson aged 25 from Leeds.

Sadly no drawings or photographs of the first house in its flush of youth and shining stone have come to light, but it was recorded as containing six bedrooms. It is most likely that the facade was much the same as today, apart from the darkened stone and the extensions to both sides. When first completed, it must have been very impressive, constructed of the best of local millstone grit stone. This coarse grained sandstone with conspicuous quartz pebbles probably came from quarries at Weetwood (now known as The Hollies), or from the Meanwood quarries in the woods high above Meanwood park. The Headingley/Meanwood area was a vast source of stone, and was listed as being home to 20 working quarries in 1847.

In the early days the coach house, stable and any garden sheds were separate buildings against the left hand (west) boundary line. A few conditions had been built into the sales document by James Fox to safeguard his property, such as insisting that no chimney be erected within 20 yards of the western boundary of the plot and a very specific instruction that the new owner had to "with all possible speed, erect, make and construct and forever hereafter maintain a sunken fence on the western boundary line".

Isaac Israel was a partner in Julius Israel & Co., Foreign Wool Merchants & Importers, of 8, Alfred Street, off Boar Lane in Leeds city centre. During his tenure of Wheatfield Lodge, Isaac Israel changed his name to Isaac Irwell.

Following his death, his trustees Herman Israel and Isaac Storey offered for sale in 1874 the 'large and improved' Wheatfield Lodge. It was not on the market long, and was sold on 6th October 1874, for an undisclosed sum to Mr. Richard Buckton, who at the time was living with his family at Cumberland Lodge, in Ashwood Terrace, Headingley. Buckton was another self-made man, whose business centred on the manufacture of linen at his company, Buckton & May, with its Hunslet Linen works situated on Goodman Street, south Leeds.

The 1881 Census records that residents at Wheatfield Lodge included Richard, his wife, four children, a sister and three servants, with a coachman, his wife and two children living in the newly built No. 13, Wood Lane Gate House. Three years later, Richard Buckton put Wheatfield Lodge, Hereditaments and premises on the market. The conveyance, dated 19th May 1884, records the sale to Mr. Joseph Nicholson for the incredible sum in those days of £5,500.00. This was a fortune in the 1880s, but the house as it stood only formed the basis of future plans for this historic house.

Nora and Arthur Nicholson setting out for a day's golf just prior to the 1st World War, golf clubs tucked in behind the driver. During the war this car was fitted with an overhead framework to support a large gas bag which allowed up to 20 miles of local running on one filling.
(Collection Mr. C. Nicholson)

CHAPTER 3
WHEATFIELD LODGE, NO 11 WOOD LANE – THE ULTIMATE 'GENTLEMAN'S RESIDENCE'

The house passed into the hands of the man who was to have the most profound effect on the property in the Spring of 1884.

The typical prosaic legal terms of the Indentures record the purchase by Mr. Joseph Nicholson 'of that messuage or dwelling house called Wheatfield Lodge' from Mr. Richard Buckton, for the not inconsiderable sum of £5,500.00, signed, sealed and delivered on the l9th May 1884.

A late 19th century studio portrait of Joseph Nicholson in characteristic pose with cigar - the owner of 'Wheatfield' from 1884 to 1918. (Collection Mr. C. Nicholson)

A complete change of business interest had attracted Joseph to Leeds following the offer of a partnership in the family's South Leeds Chemical Company. John Carr Nicholson was then head of John Nicholson & Son Ltd., with its expanding sulphuric acid producing plant in Church Street, off Balm Road, Hunslet. The partnership agreement offered 25% of the profits initially, building up in increments over 5, 7 and 10 years to 75%, sufficient inducement for Joseph to relinquish his

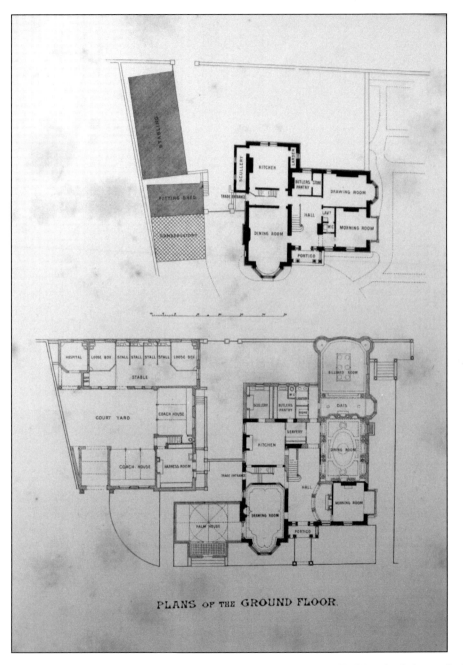

PLANS OF THE GROUND FLOOR.

Above & Right: The illustrations at the top of each plan show the house as it was up to the mid-1880s and at the bottom of each plan show the house as partiatially rebuilt and extended in the early 1890s.

16

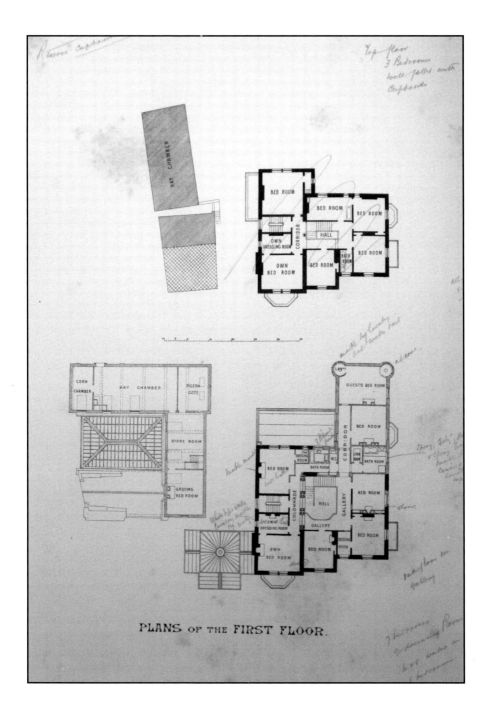

PLANS of the FIRST FLOOR.

manufacturing jewellery business in Halifax and move to Leeds with his wife Elisabeth (nee Midgeley) to look for a suitable family home. John Carr Nicholson lived in considerable style at 'Moorfield' on Alma Road, Headingley, which is probably why Joseph found Wheatfield Lodge on the adjacent corner of Wood Lane.

The house was initially more than adequate for the family, but with Joseph's increasing prosperity it was inevitable that he wanted to see this reflected in his home. After a few years he started to plan a most ambitious series of alterations and extensions to the 'Lodge', which would, on completion, leave the house ostensibly as we see it today.

To translate his ideas into reality, he turned to a young local architect who specialised in large houses with very fine interior detail - Thomas Butler Wilson, F.R.I.B.A., (1859-1942), who had taken over the Headingley practice of his father, James Wilson, in 1884. Thomas had been educated at Leeds Grammar School and Leeds University prior to being articled to London architect Charles Bell F.R.I.B.A. On his return to

The impressive 1893 Palm House or Conservatory, supplied by W. Richardson & Co. Ltd., of Darlington. Entered by double doors from the drawing room, this fabulous structure lasted to the end of the 2nd World War. Indications of its size can be gauged by looking at the curved mark on the end of the house, still visible after all these years.

Leeds, in addition to the Headingley office, he opened new branches in London and Harrogate before becoming a Fellow of the Royal Institute of British Architects in 1893.

The conversion and extension works were estimated to take in the region of one year to eighteen months, so once the detailed drawings were approved in April 1892 the house was completely cleared, with the exception of Joseph's study, titled on the plans as 'the morning room', and this light 19'0" x 16'3" room, to the right of the front door, is now used as the Hospice chapel. The study was piled high with books, paintings etc., and sealed for the duration of the builders' occupation, which may well account for the room having far less ornate plasterwork than the other main reception rooms.

To say that the conversion work was carried out regardless of cost would be an understatement! All the detail and plasterwork was quite outstanding. The dining room, to the left of the front door, became the Adam style 24'0" x 18'6" drawing room, with a fine coved ceiling. The new dining room, second door on the right from the front

"Wheatfield Lodge", Headingley, Yorks: The Billiard Room

door, was in a bold Georgian style, 26'0" long x 20'0" wide, with its parquetry floor well illuminated by three 'French' windows.

The quality of the design and decoration of the conversion merited it being featured in the pages of 'The Architect', prior to it being published in large format form by B.T. Batsford of High Holborn, London, very well illustrated with specially commissioned photographs by Mr. Charles Latham.

Butler Wilson's own words describe the dining room as 'an essentially Georgian room, its ivory and gold enrichments frame silk-brocaded panels, in some of which are placed Ormolu Electroliers from authentic models. Chippendale's best manner pervades the furniture, whilst an old Persian carpet almost covers the parquetry flooring'.

The other large new room to the rear of the house was the extensive 32'0" x 20'0" Billiard Room, decorated in the Adam style, with a dais at one end overlooking the superb Burrows & Watt billiard table, which, along with all the fitments, was finished in polished mahogany. The surrounding carpet was specially woven to size, with the centre cut out!

The architect's pièce de résistance was the main entrance hall and staircase - Caen stone, white alabaster, and marbles from Genoa and Pavonazza form the component parts of the peristyle (curved colonnade with three columns) on the right hand side of the main hall, which now contains the Hospice reception desk.

Entrance Hall

19

Wheatfield, Headingley.

Reproduced from a turn of the century postcard.
Prominent is the tall white Acacia tree in the raised flower
bed and the splendid Palm House. It looks as if Nora Nicholson
has set out the big lawn as a putting green.
(Collection Mrs. M. McLaughlin)

"Wheatfield Lodge", Headingley, Yorks:
The Staircase

"Wheatfield Lodge", Headingley, Yorks: The Hall

"Wheatfield Lodge", Headingley, Yorks: The Dining Room

20

"Wheatfield Lodge", Headingley, Yorks: The Gallery

To complement the overall Italian theme, the walls were 'treated' in a tender Pompeian red, with the woodwork generally finished with ivory enamel, contrasting well with the doors of polished mahogany. The floor is Italian marble mosaic and the staircase is white Sicilian marble with a mahogany balustrade, supported on wrought iron balusters of the highest possible craftmanship. The ironwork is in the form of silver leaf, covering rich fruit and flowers, all subdued by Golden-Ambered lacquer.

All the installation of the expensive Italian stone work was entrusted to a team of Sicilian masons. A fitting testimonial to their skills, it still looks as magnificent to this day.

The staircase leads to the gallery (one could never use the word 'landing' in such a house), with its colonnade on one side formed from marble, alabaster and stone. The floor, or pavement as it was termed in those days, was made from white Sicilian marble.

The illumination to this palatial area was provided by an Electrolier (an electric chandelier) in Ormolu, a gold coloured copper alloy. This flamboyant creation is recorded as being a replica of that in the Bibliotheque Mazarine and, as a last artistic touch, it was hung centrally by means of a silken rope.

Worthy of note is the central heating system which was installed, with large cast iron radiators being fed from the boiler-house within the new stable block. Far more progressive was the introduction of electric lighting to supplement the existing gas supply. This wonder of the age was still in its infancy, the first Leeds generating company having been established in premises on Whitehall Road in December 1892, with the descriptive title of 'The Yorkshire House-to-House Electric Company'. The council soon realised the potential business which would become available, and six years later they moved to take over the ownership of what was eventually to become a main public utility. It is most probable that power for Wheatfield Lodge was generated by a small plant installed in the boiler-house. As an indication of how innovative this system was, statistics record that only 2% of Leeds dwellings had electricity by the outbreak of war in 1914 - truly Wheatfield Lodge was a house for the 20th century!

The first floor, in its revised layout, consisted of seven bedrooms, all main ones having lavatories and hot and cold water, three dressing rooms (one with a bath), plus a 'capital' bathroom and a servants' bathroom. On the third floor was a three room servants' flat, which was left untouched by the extension and modification work.

The interior of the house was a triumph for Butler Wilson, despite the restraints of altering someone else's work, but he had a completely free hand when it came to the brand new coach house and stable block. The old outbuildings adjacent to

"Wheatfield Lodge", Headingley, Yorks: The Stables & Coach House

the west side of the house, consisting of potting sheds, stables and a conservatory, were demolished, but still more space was required for the grand plan. This was resolved on the 9th March 1892, when a strip of land 30'0" wide, along the western boundary between Wood Lane and Alma Road, was purchased from the next door estate of Arthur Frederick Lawrence Hepton, who placed some restrictive covenants on future building work. He insisted that any new structures must be stone-faced, and that there should be no windows, skylights, door, or other openings, in the walls facing towards the Hepton property.

A high stone dividing wall was erected between the two gardens, and at the north end, where it joined on to the new coach house, it was heightened to totally hide the new building from the neighbour's view. The drawings for the new detached coach house and stable block were approved in April 1892, and a very palatial structure it turned out to be, described by the architect as:- 'Rusticated courses, heavily modillioned cornices combined with blocked columns and archivolts, indicate a mood eminently Georgian' - I think we can take his word for it!!

This impressive building was entered through wrought iron gates and an archway and short tunnel, large enough to allow the passing of any horse-drawn coach, an attractive detail being the sculptured head of a horse in sandstone mounted over the keystone of the arch. After 20'0" the tunnel opened out into a large glazed courtyard with spaces for up to six vehicles on two sides, all fitted with revolving shutter doors. Along the wall backing on to Alma Road was the stable block, with stalls for four horses, two loose boxes, and a space designated as a hospital area for sick horses. On a later plan this was recorded as a workshop, probably relating to the days when Wheatfield became motorised. Corn and hay were stored in roof chambers, to be fed down individual chutes, as required, into the stable area. On the ground floor, nearest the house, was a large harness room, completely fitted out with pitch pine harness cupboards with plate glass doors. Directly above was the groom's bedroom, behind

Turn of the century elegance of Joseph Nicholson's coachman Charles Baldock waiting at the front door with the immaculate carriage and pair. (Collection Mrs. M. McLaughlin)

which was a general store, and in the back corner was a large room designated as The Pigeon Cote. The finishing touch, rising above, was the slender circular turret capped with a copper covered dome surmounted with a tall elegant weather vane.

The newly extended villa and attendant coach house presented a most noble facade, but even this was surpassed when the large Palm House (or conservatory) was added to the corner of the drawing room. This mini 'Crystal Palace' was entered via double doors from the corner of the drawing room, or by steps leading up from the front carriage drive.

Within the next few years another glazed extension was added to the front of the coach house to form an 'L' shaped greenhouse, or what, in late Victorian days, was called a Tomato House.

Family group circa 1914 near the front door. Joseph Nicholson second from the left with daughter Nora and son-in-law Arthur at the right hand side. (Collection Mr. C. Nicholson)

So it was, in 1893, that Joseph Nicholson and his wife, and their grown-up family - son Midgley and daughters Eleanor (Nan) and Nora Isabel - returned to their fabulous house. The number of people in service required to run Wheatfield Lodge has not been recorded, but the live-in housekeeper was Spring, and the coachman Baldock and his family lived in the Gate House just inside the main gate, No. 13 Wood Lane. Baldock was a very smart and trusted employee whose granddaughter, Mary McLaughlin, treasures a gold watch inscribed - PRESENTED TO CHARLES BALDOCK by JOSEPH NICHOLSON (HEADINGLEY) IN 20 YEARS OF FAITHFUL SERVICE AS COACHMAN - AUGUST 23RD 1907

One of Baldock's regular duties was to take Mr. Nicholson and his brother over to the North Eastern Railway Station at Headingley to join the train for Leeds. On his return he always let the Station Master know if he was travelling next day so that the train could be held up for a few minutes should he be a little late.

Joseph Nicholson would appear to be far removed from the archetypal stern Victorian papa, and enjoyed having friends in for games of billiards. They had competitions to see who could climb beneath the table and negotiate all the legs without putting a foot on the floor! He was also very fond of shooting - he and his shooting friends were known as 'the unholy trinity'!!

The younger daughter of the house, Nora Isabel, was quite obviously 'the apple of her father's eye', who, after education at a French finishing school, where she met up with her future husband's sisters, became quite a liberated lady for that time. She held one

A glorious record of a high summer Edwardian Wedding at Wheatfield on 12th July 1920, when Nora Isbabel Nicholson married Arthur Nicholson. The photographers 'Rosemont' of Leeds & Bradford, recorded that enlargements could be produced of up to life size! They must have had quite an enlarger in their dark room!! (All from the Wheatfield Collection presented by Mr. C. Nicholson.)

of the first driving licences in Leeds, around 1900, was a founder member of Alwoodley Golf Club, and also played at Headingley and Ganton Clubs. No mean billiards player, she could regularly 'chalk up' a 40 break. A resourceful young lady, whilst driving one day she lost a tyre, so borrowed rope from a farmer, wrapped it around the wheel and drove on to Ganton. After a six year engagement she married Arthur Nicholson (not related), who sold his business interests in the silk trade in Macclesfield and acquired the Horatio Crowther Chemical Company in Armley, Leeds, but eventually sold out when invited by Joseph Nicholson to join the family business in Hunslet around 1918.

Following the death of her mother in 1913, Nora Isabel moved back to Wheatfield Lodge with her husband, daughter and one year old son, Claud, and effectively took over the running of the house for her father, after crossing swords with Spring, the housekeeper, who during Mrs. Nicholson's illness had assumed total control.

We are indebted to the early childhood memories of Mr. Claud Nicholson, who for a few short years lived at Wheatfield Lodge, attended by a succession of Nannies in the lovely nursery in the front bedroom which is now the Matron/Manager's office.

The young Nicholsons in November 1915. Claud, 3 years and Joyce 18 months old. Their nursery was to become Matron's Office on conversion of the house. (Collection Mr. C. Nicholson)

He recalls how grandfather always had time for a game or a chat when he returned home, and how Joseph had a great love of cigars and kept a goodly range in stock.

After 1914, and the outbreak of 'the war to end all wars', things inevitably changed. It was not long before the horses were all requisitioned for war service, by which time the coach house was becoming a garage. One or two chauffeurs came, and went. One lost his job when Joseph walked round the car only to find that it had been cleaned only on the side he normally used! Once or twice a week the chauffeur had a nice run out to Middlesmoor in the Nidd Valley to fill several containers with fresh water. Joseph could not stand Leeds water, and refused to drink it, but he could manage the stronger Harrogate Spa water, and regularly went to 'take the waters'.

During this period the coach house garaged a wide variety of vehicles. One of the first was a chassis with two interchangeable bodies - one hard top, one open - an early form of convertible. Nora Isabel had a small open car for a while, but during the war ran a saloon fitted with a roof gas bag. This was charged from the gas mains in the Palm House, and could provide energy to cover up to 20 miles on a filling, enabling her to travel around the area performing her charitable work.

Joseph's last car was, inevitably, a Rolls Royce, with the registration U323, the driving of which was entrusted to Mr. Sayner, the Nicholson's last chauffeur, who eventually started up his own garage.

One of Joseph Nicholson's great passions was shooting, and to enjoy this to the full he acquired a 'shoot' at Middlesmoor near the head of the Nidd Valley above Pateley

Bridge, north of Harrogate, and initially furnished Fairfield House in Pateley Bridge during the shooting season. In later years he also took over the public house in Middlesmoor for six weeks to house his shooting party of close friends.

The idyllic life style at Wheatfield Lodge sadly ended with Joseph Nicholson's death at the age of 70, on the 24th March 1918. In his obituary he was listed as Chairman of Directors of John Nicholson & Son (Ltd), Hunslet Chemical Works, a director of Yorkshire Penny Bank, and a Commissioner of Income Tax.

In accordance with his will, of the 30th January 1915, his executor - son-in-law Arthur Nicholson - after settling with his family in the Chapeltown area of Leeds, arranged the sale of Wheatfield Lodge by auction on Wednesday, 29th October 1919, organised by Messrs. Hepper & Sons, East Parade, Leeds. For interested parties, Hepper's produced and had printed by King & Son Ltd, Halifax, a sumptuously illustrated brochure describing the house, and conditions of sale. The first page heading, worthy of note, was - 'SUPERBLY APPOINTED RESIDENCE KNOWN AS WHEATFIELD'. The title 'Lodge' had been rejected. There were a few items to be removed from the drawing room including 'the mantelpiece and interior and overmantel, two electric brackets over two electric hanging bowls, plus a large painted cupboard in the attic'. To cover the vendors, it was noted that 'no compensation will be made for any damage that may be done by removal'.

The other major item which had already gone was the billiard table, sold to Nelsons Billiard Saloon over Leeds Market, where it became the No. 1 table. Claud Nicholson recalls playing on it years later when he was active in the Hunslet Workshop Billiards League.

One of the inevitable consequences of the sale of a large house was the breaking up of the team of service staff. Probably the first to go was Healy, the under-gardener, who later requested a reference. This was duly penned by Arthur Nicholson on 7th February 1919, and this tiny document has survived and reads as follows:

'I have pleasure in stating Healy has been in our employ about 1 year, as under-gardener and we don't wish to employ a more willing and reliable worker.

yrs truly,
A. Nicholson.'

On the back he added 'Healy leaves this employment owing to the death of his employer, Mr. Joseph Nicholson'

CHAPTER 4
WHEATFIELD BETWEEN THE WARS

The next residents of 'Wheatfield' (No. 11 Wood Lane) were Mr. Thomas Gill and his wife Edna, who also owned 'Elmbank' on Bradford Road, Cleckheaton. Thomas Gill was an entrepreneur - a director of numerous companies and manufacturers, mostly relating to the textile trade, and he purchased his Headingley residence for £6,300.00 at auction. Sadly, his tenure of this beautiful house was relatively short, due to his death on the 31st March 1922. The appointed executors, sons William and George Edward, along with Joseph and Arnold Milner, lost no time in selling Wheatfield and premises on behalf of Edna Gill (named as 'the Diviseel') on the 25th May 1923, recorded as 'free from all incumbrances' for the sum of £5,750.00.

Bronze plaque at Leeds General Infirmary depicting Walter Thompson, M.R.C.S. Eng. L.R.C.P. LOND. (1887), F.R.C.S. Eng. (1891) to record his service as Senior Honorary Surgeon from 1909 until his death in 1924, during which time he purchased Wheatfield in 1923 for £5,750.

The new owner was Mr. Walter Thompson, M.R.C.S. Eng., L.R.C.P. Lond. (1887), F.R.C.S. Eng (1891). Born in 1866, the son of a Wharfedale farmer, he was to have a glittering career leading to becoming Senior Honorary Surgeon at Leeds General Infirmary, at a time when honorary surgeons were not salaried consultants, as in more recent times. To give an indication of this man's many faceted career it can be summarised thus:

Following his medical education at Leeds Medical School and in Berlin, where he lodged with Moynihan, in June 1888 he was appointed second house physician and in October of the same year became house surgeon to Mr. Jessop. After being resident medical officer at the Ida Hospital, resident casualty officer at the Infirmary and resident surgical officer (1893-6) he spent a period in general practice, and was anaesthetist at the Infirmary from 1896 to 1899 when he resigned on being appointed surgeon to the Hospital for Women and Children. In December 1902 he was elected assistant surgeon at the Infirmary, becoming surgeon in 1909.

During the First World War he served in Serbia and Salonika. In the University he was lecturer in the practice of surgery. He was also surgeon to the Leeds Public Dispensary. He carried out many abdominal operations in cottages and country houses in Yorkshire, far from hospitals.

Walter's wife, Ann Elizabeth Thompson, was also a doctor, but not then in practice, and they were to found a medical dynasty. All three of their daughters - Daphne, May and Jean - became doctors, and son Samuel went on to become an Orthopaedic Consultant.

Unfortunately, Walter Thompson had barely a year to enjoy his life at Wheatfield before his untimely death on the 12th May 1924. In his will, dated 11th August 1906, his wife Elizabeth was named as sole Executrix, and 27 years passed before she finally parted with her beloved family home, apart from a tiny area of land at the rear of the house on the south side of Alma Road on the 26th September 1936, purchased by the city of Leeds for the construction of an electricity sub-station. Mrs. Jean F. Wilson (nee Thompson) recalled 'a near idyllic family life' with the house staffed by a cook, two parlour maids, and a chauffeur - those were the days! 'We were a normal family. We enjoyed tennis on the lawn, later transferring to the Headingley Tennis Club to save trouble. The Club was in the grounds of the Lupton's house at the end of Wood Lane where it meets Headingley Lane. We did not ride, so that beautifully fitted out stable block was a playground when we were young, and a garage later on.'

'Another playground was the cellar - my father had kept wine in the wine cellar, and washing was done in a huge copper boiler in the middle cellar, and that point, adjoining Alma Road, was known as the 'earthquake' owing to the upheaval of the concrete floor. I also recall when a workman on the roof put a foot and leg through the coloured glass skylight over the hall - he was terrified, and the replacement glass was never as good as the original'.

She also had fond memories of the dances held in the dining room every winter, and the warm conservatory with underfloor heating, and its central palm bed. Outside was a clipped Hawthorn tree, but the main feature was the fabulous white Acacia tree. Over the years this must have grown to massive proportions judging by the diameter of the stump still in the raised bed just around the left hand corner from the front door of the present annexe block. Her mother also recalled that Queen Alexandra once visited Wheatfield to look at the hall and staircase. One last point - the whole family were sorry to hear that 'Wheatfield' became 'Wheatfields' - in their opinion 'the area is not big enough for the plural, but it was a lovely home'.

Since becoming a Hospice Wheatfields has always played a very important part within the community, but its involvement with the young people of Headingley goes back to the early 1930s, when the upstairs rooms of the coach house were first made available for the use of the local Boy Scouts troop.

It was noted by the Rev. F. C. Giddins, curate of St. Michael's & All Angels Church, in the Headingley Parish Magazine for December 1925, that he was of the opinion that the Boys Club at the Church 'had served its purpose and done good work during the past six years, but I have felt for some time past that the time has come when we might, with advantage, start a troop of Boy Scouts again'. In the January issue of the magazine he recorded that the 13th North West Troop was being introduced with the

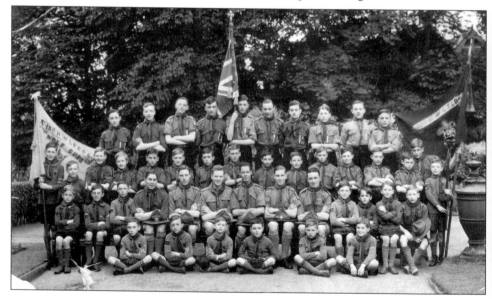

The 13th North West Leeds Scouts & Cubs photographed at Wheatfields in the early 1930s. 4th from the right on the back row is Patrol Leader of the Lion Patrol Reginald Simpson who later became a Church Warden at St. Michael's & All Angels as well as a volunteer for many years at the Hospice.
(Collection Mr. R. Simpson)

help of Messrs. Arthur Simpson, a territorial army officer and architect as Scoutmaster, and Martin Dykes as Assistant Scoutmaster, who were both experienced and keen scouts. Three patrols were introduced - The Eagles, The Bulldogs, and The Lions, and they were to be resplendent in their smart blue and red 'Neckers'.

In the March 1926 issue of the Parish Magazine it was recorded that 'a very impressive little ceremony was held in Church on Sunday evening, March 9th, in the presence of a very large congregation - (one would like to see a congregation like it every Sunday evening). It was the dedication of the Union Jack at enrolment of the Troop. We were honoured with the presence of the District Scout and Cub Masters'. Worthy of note was that the flag was carried by the 16 year old patrol leader of The Lion patrol, Reginald Simpson (no relation of the Scoutmaster) who, along with his No. 2, Howard Bickerdyke, were to become long serving Church Wardens at St. Michael's. Reginald Simpson was to become a regular volunteer in the Treasurer's Office at Wheatfields Hospice for many years.

In 1937 the coach house became the regular meeting place for the newly formed Headingley branch of the 'Junior Imperial League', known nationally as the 'Imps', or, following the second world war, as 'The Young Conservatives'.

The three leading lights in the formation and organisation of this new venture were a young married couple, Denis and Margaret Gledhill, and Margaret's sister Nancy Miller. Young people with a strong social conscience, they had already hired and arranged dances in the ballroom of the Leeds Motor Club on Woodhouse Lane to raise funds for the 'Linen League', of the Leeds General Infirmary.

Margaret Gledhill takes up the story in her own words: 'There were no youth clubs then apart from things like Hunslet Boys' Club - very little else, a few local dances, and that was about it. There was nowhere we could get together, talk, and create. My mother's family were an old Headingley family, and we just seemed to draw in more and more young people. Denis was an old Grammar School boy with lots of friends, and it just gathered momentum. We approached Mrs Thompson for the use of the stables, and she let us have it for £5 a year rent and £5 a year towards the rates. She insisted that the place was kept scrupulously clean, and we could assure her there would be no parking problems at all as not one of us had a car - it was a bicycle, or walk! The age group was about 15 - 24, and we attracted a lot of students from Leeds University's Devonshire Hall, as at that time the University had no active political party.

We started by decorating the rooms above the stable, which still contained a few bales of hay. The rooms were unfurnished, so after colour washing with distemper we begged and borrowed any old furniture - tables, chairs, etc., - and repaired them if necessary - we were all very young, enthusiastic, and very active!

We had meetings on Mondays, Fridays and Saturdays, starting with Whist Drives on Mondays for parents and friends. To raise money, the entrance fee was one shilling. People attending were asked to please bring and donate a cup, plate, and/or items of cutlery with them, so that we could provide tea and biscuits. We begged small prizes until we could afford to purchase them, and local traders supported us (a tradition carried on today, in support of the hospice), and many sent their younger members of the family to join what they recognised as a good influence on young people.

We also arranged a Craft or Hobby Room, which was available for people wishing to paint, or with any creative interest (another parallel with today's activities in the Day Hospice). One of the popular pastimes was the building of scale model aircraft.

On Friday evenings we often had a dance or 'hop' in the actual stable area (ideal for barn dances) and again, the fee was around a shilling. We would attract 50 - 60 people. These took the form of what would now be called a 'disco', except in those peaceful days the gramophone arrived on the back of a bicycle, or was pushed to Wheatfield in a pram, and everyone was on their way home by 10 - 10.30 p.m.

Meetings and lectures were arranged, providing a forum that enabled those attending to debate their views and to listen to visiting speakers, ranging from Leeds Councillors, Members of Parliament, and local Aldermen. In those days war clouds were gathering over Europe, and it would not be long before these young people would be called upon to 'fight for their country', even if they were not allowed to vote!!

The stable room was open every Sunday evening after church services for a chat over a cup of tea, coffee, or lemonade. No alcohol was allowed on the premises in any event, and so it continued until May 1940. Once war was declared, thirty of the Headingley Imps volunteered for service. The remaining members of the group blacked out all the coach house and stable windows in order to continue evening meetings. The final 'hop' was arranged for February 16th 1940, the last bales of hay in the stable added the finishing touch to what was entitled a 'hobos' dance. The call to arms decimated the membership, and soon the chairman, Denis Gledhill, joined the forces, and his wife Margaret was elected to the post. Her term of office was relatively short, as she terminated the meetings after the 17th May 1940. The stable was locked up, and the keys returned to Mrs. Thompson with a letter of gratitude for her support.'

As Mrs. Gledhill recalls, 'we were never to return again to Wheatfield, but more poignant is seeing the names of young friends from the old days recorded on the War Memorial.'

In 1935 Mary Thompson had married Dr. Frederick William Webster, the official photograph being taken in front of the house, with the bride's two sisters and her sister-in-law all acting as bridesmaids.

During the early years of the war, the citizens of Leeds fully expected the city would be a prime target for the enemy bombers, and with this in mind, Mrs. Thompson made available to neighbours Wheatfield's ample cellars for use as an air raid shelter. Due to the variation in height of the ground these could be entered at ground level at the rear of the house. Pauline Mellor of 25 Grove Road recalls that during the few alerts experienced, between 12 and 20 people would take shelter and Mr. Wilkinson used to come in to light the combustion stove to take off the chill.

Jean Thompson married Dr. Terry Wilson in 1941, but wartime austerity ruled out any photographs at Wheatfield. In fact it was the last family event to take place, as the house was requisitioned soon after by the Ministry of Works for the duration of the war. Dr. Jean Wilson recalled 'the family bade a sad farewell to their home - but not as sad as it might have been, because fortunately we had by that time all left home'.

Miss Dorothy Smith in her uniform when she worked for the N.E. Region H.Q. of the National Fire Service, Wheatfield; from Jan. 1944 to June 1947, rising from a shorthand typist to the rank of Assistant Group Officer. (Photo Mrs. D. Fletcher)

CHAPTER 5
WHEATFIELD HOUSE GOES TO WAR!

When the clouds of war swept over Europe again in 1939 it was necessary to establish a Regional Commissioner's office in Leeds, which was to be a regional seat of Government in the event of invasion. This was considered by many to be a distinct possibility after Germany's systematic domination of most of Western Europe. The first regional office was in Bishopgate Street, but lack of space forced a move to bigger premises at 36 Park Row.

Leeds was fortunate in only suffering nine air raids during the duration of the second World War, and by far the worst of these occurred on the night of 14/15th March 1941, when two well-spaced out waves of enemy aircraft crossed the east coast heading for the city. Their targets were probably the railway stations, goods yards, the nearby Gas Works and engineering companies, and the munitions factory 'Barnbow' in the suburb of Cross Gates. Ironically, it was the front of the 1821 building in Park Row housing the Leeds City Museum which received a direct hit from a high explosive bomb, which also, sadly, claimed the life of one of the Regional Commissioner's motor-cycle messengers, who had just left a nearby office.

This raid was too close for comfort, and despite the newly established 'War Room' having been set up in the basement of the Park Row office block, the leafy suburbs seemed a safer bet. The transfer of the R.C. Office and War Room to 'Wheatfield' took place, with additional office accommodation in Castle Grove Masonic Lodge and

'Redhill' on Shire Oak Road. Wheatfield was already home to the administration of the North Eastern Region of the National Fire Service, and new buildings, air raid shelters and two garages had been hastily erected in the front gardens, and the gate-house - 13 Wood Lane - had been demolished, the last residents being Mr. Axel, the Wheatfield gardener, his wife and son Willy.

At the nerve centre of the Regional Headquarters was the all important 'War Room' with its bank of telephones and teleprinter staffed around the clock. This was not established in the basement of the house, but in an air raid shelter type building within the grounds. All forms of information were assimilated, including daily regional reports from all the essential services including electricity generating stations and gas works.

Three smart Fire Service ladies with very '40s hairstyles! Mrs. Dorothy Clements (nee Smith) in the middle worked at Wheatfield from 1943 to 1947. (Collection Mrs. D. Fletcher)

The war changed the lives of many people profoundly, and we are at least able to get a flavour of what it was like to be so involved at the regional centre of Government during the hostilities, from the recollections of people who still survive.

One such person is Mrs. Nora Moody, a young civil servant in the Mineral Valuer's office in Leeds, who married Stanley, a serving Army Officer, before he was posted to

35

India in 1940. The ban on married personnel resulted in her joining the R.C.O. in Bishopgate Street as a shorthand typist, and the following year she moved to the larger offices in Park Row as part of the initial team of typists under the supervision of Frances Sutherland. In 1941, when they transferred to Wheatfield, they were soon joined by many others to form a typing pool in the ballroom at Castle Grove Masonic Hall, and to fill offices at nearby Redhill.

Supervising the typists at the two outstations of Wheatfield was Miss Muriel Jean Baildon, who was seconded from the General Post Office Administration sector in October 1941. She still remembers how fit she was in those days, due to walking between the three offices with only the occasional use of a push bike. The canteen for all the personnel was provided at Castle Grove, but the two ladies involved in fire-watching could breakfast in the fire service canteen housed in Wheatfield. This was a treat, as only the Fire Service provided scrambled dried eggs for breakfast in those days of harsh rationing! Being in the centre of all available information, these two ladies were often told in the early hours that it was unlikely there would be a raid, and were able to get their heads down in a room (once the groom's accommodation above the stable block). This was not recalled with much relish by Mrs. Moody, as the grey woollen army blankets on the two camp beds provided were rather hard and scratchy.

As the raids eventually became less likely, Miss Baildon often started the evening with a visit to the Lounge Cinema along with her friend, Nora Moody, for an hour or two of light entertainment.

Leading the high powered team at Wheatfield was Sir William Bartholomew, the Regional Commissioner. His Military Liaison Officer was Major McCorquodale, and the Royal Air Force equivalent was Lord Mountgarrett, assisted by an Air Vice Marshall. The police had a powerful presence, headed by the Chief Inspector of Constabulary, Sir Francis Brook, who spent a lot of his time touring the forces in his very large region. Based full time in Leeds were Acting Inspector of Constabulary, Major G. W. R.. Ahearn, and Superintendent G.O. Gilbert, Chief Inspector R. A. Abbiss, Inspector H. Amble (who became Chief Constable of Bradford after the war). Sergeant E. Staines (who later became Chief Constable of Bradford), and last, but by no means least, was Police Constable G. Newland. Between them the department was manned round the clock.

The police contingent were constantly busy, for in addition to normal duties they were responsible for keeping a close watch on all possible forms of subversive activities, and producing the daily 'Bomb Report' which covered all forms of enemy activity in the broad acres stretching out to the East Coast.

Telephone: LEEDS 54111

All letters to be addressed to :—

CHIEF REGIONAL FIRE OFFICER

and the following reference quoted :

PPB/DC.

Your reference

NATIONAL FIRE SERVICE

NORTH EASTERN REGION HEADQUARTERS,
"WHEATFIELD,"
WOOD LANE,
HEADINGLEY,
LEEDS, 6.

12th June, 1947.

To whom it may concern.

Mrs. D.Clements has been a member of the National Fire Service since 25th January, 1943, and has been employed as a Shorthand Typist. She gained promotion as follows :-

29th April, 1943 to the rank of Leading Firewoman.
22nd Oct., 1943   "   "   "   Senior Leading Firewoman.
10th March, 1944 "   "   "   Assistant Group Officer.

In the first place Mrs.Clements was a member of the Typists Pool but on her promotion to the rank of Leading Firewoman she was placed in charge of the Pool. Since her appointment to the rank of Assistant Group Officer on the 10th March, 1944, she has been my personal private Secretary.

Mrs.Clements has at all times carried out her duties in a most satisfactory manner, in addition to being a first class Shorthand Typist she is also a very capable Secretary and entirely trustworthy in the handling of confidential matters.

I have no hesitation whatever in saying that she is in all respects highly suitable for any employment of a Secretarial nature.

[signature]

CHIEF REGIONAL FIRE OFFICER.

Headed notepaper of the National Fire Service during the 2nd World War.

As an indication of the importance of 'Wheatfield' during the last war note the number of Fire Service staff caught in this 1943 group photograph. (Photo Mrs. D. Fletcher)

To assist the police, Mrs. Moody was assigned to this section, and as much of her work was inevitably top secret, it was always interesting. She recalls that the officers were not used to a female member of staff and fussed round her, making cups of tea. One unusual daily chore was the morning check of the lines into the War Room, which, in direct contact with London, was staffed round the clock by teams of six women, and the lines were checked by passing along a coded message to London.

From 1942, for about two years, volunteer motorcycle riders, in pairs, manned a room in the main annexe block in case of invasion. There were about twenty enthusiastic riders who gave their time, which excused them from joining the Home Guard or having to carry out fire-watching duties. One of these despatch riders was Mr. Randolph Bradley, a young engineer with the firm of McCullock & Newitt, whose work was classified as a reserved occupation. A motorcycle fan, his pride and joy was his powerful 600cc 1932 model 'Panther', Reg. UB9-764. The R.C.O. provided their volunteer riders with crash helmets, three quarter length coats, and trousers, plus a free road fund licence issued by the Defence Of The Realms Act (known as DORA), and additional petrol coupons. Riders were responsible for the upkeep of their machines and for insurance cover. Instructors from the Royal Corps of Signals gave regular lectures on the servicing of their motorcycles and took them out on practice runs at a rate of tuppence farthing a mile - one new penny in today's currency! Expenses had to be collected from the control office of the team at Marsdens Mill on Dewsbury Road, where Mr. Marsden had put together his team of riders. No mean rider himself, he owned a powerful trio of personal British classic machines, such as a 'Vincent', a 'Brough Superior' and a 'Norton'.

Two riders were based in the annexe at Wheatfield, in a bare office with a telephone and two iron frame Z beds for the 12 hour shift from 8 p.m. to 8 a.m. every night.

They were classified as riders "A" and "B", and if only one rider was needed it was always "A", but they changed over the next time on duty. Needless to say, not one of the motorcycles turned a wheel in anger, and they got together when the team was disbanded and had a party at the Union tavern. It was fortunate that none of the team had to turn out that night!

The National Fire Service North Eastern Region H.Q., based at Wheatfield, had a staff of about 50 personnel, with Chief Regional Fire Officer Mr. P. P. Booth in charge, with offices at the front of the house. One person with fond memories of the service from January 1943 to June 1947 is Dorothy Smith, who had worked at the C.W.S. Boot & Shoe factory in Meanwood Road from the age of 14 to 22. This was a reserved occupation even in the office, so she had avoided being called up when she reached 18. In January 1943, aged 22, she had to choose either the Fire Service at Wheatfield, or munitions - not a difficult choice, as she could walk from home to Wood Lane via Woodhouse Ridge.

Taken all round, it was a very good move. Wages up from £2 to just over £3 a week, and a very pleasant crowd to work with, a smart uniform, and a post as a shorthand typist. Most of the other girls in the typing pool were between 16 and 18 years old, so it was not long before Dorothy was promoted to Leading Firewoman on 29th April 1943, and by 22nd October she was supervising the typing pool elevated to the rank of Senior Leading Firewoman.

In overall charge of the massive area covered by the North Eastern No.2 Region of the National Fire Service was P. P. Booth. Inevitably he spent a lot of his time moving around his main stations, including Leeds, Hull, Sheffield and Doncaster. When his secretary left the service in March 1944, Dorothy Smith was appointed to the post and promoted to the rank of Assistant Group Officer. Second in command at Wheatfield N.F.S. Headquarters was C.P. McKinlay (Mac), very much an operational officer, and the administrative side was in the hands of Divisional Officer Raymond Cross, who undertook the centralisation of all the areas within the region.

Assistant Group Officer Dorothy Smith soon became, in effect, secretary to all three of these influential high ranking officers. In addition, she was responsible for taking shorthand notes at Divisional meetings, with up to twelve officers all talking at once! She could fill two shorthand pads during a six hour meeting, and then had to immediately type out a first draft report. Inevitably there were sad times, like the blitz on Hull, when fire stations were wiped out and many officers killed. Full reports of the losses and carnage involved had to be recorded and reported in detail, which led eventually to the centralising of 4, 5 and 6 areas, with key officers from each area moving to work at Wheatfield.

There were too many people for the annexe accommodation, with almost 70 personnel on station, so many moved upstairs into offices created from the old bedrooms. Dorothy's office was half of the old billiard room at the back, divided in two by a plasterboard wall, the other half being taken by the Catering Officer responsible for supplies to all stations. It is recalled

Regional Commissioner's Office staff group outside the house containing the all important 'War Room'. (Collection Mrs. N. Moody)

that an officer could get a better lunch at Wheatfield Fire Service centre than at home, in those 'rather thin' rationing days.

When Dorothy's fiance, Ricky Clements, came home after four years army service in Egypt, they married at Meanwood Church in 1944, and he was moved to the south of England on bomb and mine clearance around the coast for a year. Demobilisation came in 1946, the year of the 'big freeze', with icicles forming inside the office where the typists at Wheatfield had to sit in their greatcoats, trying to type with their gloves on - firefighting was very hard work that winter. Not surprisingly the Clements decided to emigrate to South Africa, and within six weeks of applying they were on the boat to Capetown, Dorothy with an excellent reference from Chief Regional Fire Officer Booth dated 12th June 1947. They went on to build a good life in South Africa, but she had given up a job worth over £6 a week, which was a good wage in 1947!

As the war ground on to its inevitable conclusion, the need for the offices in Headingley started to dwindle as more and more staff were recalled to London to take up their original careers in the Civil Service. Nora Moody moved to take up the post of secretary to the Principal Officer at Redhill on Shire Oak Road for a short time, before leaving to have her first child in 1946.

Only the Fire Office held sway at Wheatfield for the longest time before the de-nationalised service was handed back to the control of the local authorities.

Wheatfield and its workers, throughout the war, had done a fabulous job, but peacetime initially did not look so rosy.

A lady who liked to get involved - pioneer fundraising volunteer Lucy Boulton in characteristic pose working the tombola drum at a very damp 1990 Garden Party. Note the hastily prepared tabard made from a bin liner. Nothing could dampen her enthusiasm

Chef Norman Cox carving the turkey for our patients at Christmas

Niall and Raegan with Mum Lisa holding the memory box which the children have filled with possessions to remind them of their Dad

Staff of Bryan's Fish Restaurant completing a sponsored pull of Concorde to raise funds for Wheatfields

The author and Barbara Barrett
in fine style at the Garden Party

Day Hospice patient George Weston
discovering skills he never knew he had

The Day Hospice in the refurbished stable block - the arch in the far left hand corner being where the coach and horses used to enter the stable courtyard

An emotional day at Wheatfields as we arrange a wedding for Tracy - fulfilling her wish to arrive on a Harley Davidson motorbike

The Wakefield International Fleur de Lys Majorettes - a firm favourite every year at the Garden Party

The last group photograph of Royal Auxiliary Air Force 3609 Fighter Control Unit (West Riding) on the dais end of the ex billiard room, Christmas 1960. After conversion this area became one of the two four-bedded wards. (Collection F. J. Whitehead)

CHAPTER 6
FAITH, HOPE AND CHARITY

The end of hostilities in 1945 brought an inevitable sigh of relief nationwide, and heralded a period of mixed fortunes for Wheatfield. For several years an uneasy peace known as the 'cold war' prevailed, fuelled by nagging doubts about the trustworthiness of our recent allies from beyond the iron curtain. The climate created a renewed interest in civil defence, encouraged by 'scaremongers' forecasting a nuclear war, and when the fire service moved to their new area headquarters at Birkenshaw their place at Wheatfield was taken over by the civil defence volunteers for a time.

The house was never returned to its rightful owner, Mrs. Ann Elizabeth Thompson, who at the end of the war was living nearby at 2 Harrowby Road, West Park, Leeds. With all the additional outbuildings and alterations, Wheatfield could never become a private house again without a lot of expense. Presumably with this in mind, Mrs. Thompson signed the conveyance on 5th November 1951 for the sale of the old house to the Ministry of Works for £8,500, with a note on the document stating that the sale was adjudged not chargeable with stamp duty.

The Government Ministry did not hold on to the property for very long, and sold it to the Lord Mayor, Aldermen and Citizens of the City of Leeds. The conveyance, dated 13th February 1954, records:

"The premises known as Wheatfield, Wood Lane in the City of Leeds, the dwelling house with land outbuildings attached or appertaining thereto and all other buildings in the grounds thereof containing in the whole seven thousand seven hundred and fifteen square yards or thereabouts, together with all fixtures and fittings therein."

All for the sum of fifteen thousand five hundred pounds, and the sale was again adjudged not chargeable with any stamp duty.

In 1955 the Council granted a lease of the old house to 609 Squadron (The West Riding Squadron) of the Royal Auxiliary Air Force, 3609 Fighter Control Unit and 2609 Anti-Aircraft Squadron of the R.A.F. regiment, for the three to use Wheatfield as their city headquarters.

The West Riding Squadron had been established as an auxiliary volunteer squadron at Yeadon in 1936, only five years after the Leeds & Bradford Airport had been opened. New hangars were constructed to house the 'Avro Trainers' and the 'Hawker Hinds', typical bi-planes of the period used for training the highly committed enthusiastic amateur pilots. One of these was a young Leeds man Sydney Hawthorne Hanson who joined in 1937. He recalled with relish those halcyon days of flying which very soon provided pilots who became our first line of defence in the war about to engulf us.

At the outbreak of the Second World War, all auxiliaries (pilots and ground crew) received telegrams ordering them to report. Like so many others Sydney Hanson lost no time and abandoned the wagon he was scheduled to drive to Blackpool for a Leeds Foundry, jumped into his two seater M.G., and set off for Yeadon. The Squadron was soon in the thick of the action in many theatres of war before being disbanded in Germany at the end of hostilities.

After re-forming to fly from Yeadon and Church Fenton, it was time to bid farewell to their fabulous Spitfires, the jet age was at hand, and new skills were called for, not only for pilots but also for highly skilled engineers who carried out all maintenance on the aircraft. One of the last piston engine designs in service at Yeadon was the famous twin-engined 'Mosquito' which did not take to the 'hump' in the runway, particularly at night, and was not capable of taking off from there with full tanks of fuel. Pilots gaining their flying hours were compelled to call in at R.A.F. Linton in order to fill up. Jet power in the form of 'Meteors' took over, and in the 1950s the Squadron was recalled for six months active service during the Korean war.

The re-equipping of the Squadron with Vampire aircraft signalled the end of flying from Yeadon's short runway. Church Fenton's longer airstrip provided flying facilities for regular weekend flying, but unfortunately, the airbase had no accommodation for a Squadron Headquarters, and it was thus that Leeds City Council came to the rescue by making Wheatfield available.

Mr and Mrs Pollard were appointed caretakers and probably looked after the old house during its most lively period. The Officers' Mess (complete with grand piano), which doubled as the ballroom on social occasions was established in the old dining room. A bar was installed in the first room on the right (now the chapel) and a Sergeants' Mess and Corporals' Club were found space together with a games room at the back, with two snooker tables, and main offices in upstairs rooms. Frank H. Ziegler in "The Story of 609 Squadron under the White Rose" wrote: "To be used not only for social purposes but also for ground instruction. Its name was Wheatfield, it was situated in Headingley, Leeds, and in size, furnishings and amenities was worthy of the Squadron that took it over".

On Saturday evening, 9th July 1955, the opening ceremony was performed by Squadron Leader (later Wing Commander) R.P. (Roly) Beaumont at a party to remember. The house was packed as he unveiled a plaque in the hall and the rooms were decked with portraits, battle scenes and trophies. To make sure the party went with a swing, one of the large Victorian baths upstairs was filled with punch. No wonder many of the revellers were later laid out in lines in the coach house and left to recover!

They certainly had a lively social life in the squadron, but the commitment these people gave was enormous. Most attended two evenings a week straight from work and were expected to be available three weekends per month. Fighter Control had a plotting table in the coach house. They kept up with the advances in radar, along with weekend practical experience at Patrington and Bempton, as well as attending a two week summer camp, which one year involved fighter control in NATO exercises in Germany. By this time young Aircraftsman Hanson who had risen to become Flight Lieutenant Sydney Hawthorne Hanson, M.B.E. A.E.C., but better known to one and all as 'Darkie Hanson' (due to his superb black handlebar moustache so favoured by the R.A.F. during the war years) was appointed to the arduous post of 'Wine Officer'. Darkie, an engineer with a taste for fast cars, remained a fervent patriot to the end, filling the walls of his home with prints and photographs which reflected his love of speed and flying. He passed away at the age of 88 on 25th September 2000.

Inevitably the auxiliary volunteers who had given countless hours of service to 609 Squadron had to face up to final disbandment in 1957. Fighter Control Unit of Squadron 3609 remained at Wheatfield until 1961. During that period, in August 1958, Flight Lieutenant Doreen Thornton and Flight Officer Jack Marshall, two of the active personnel, were married and had their reception in the old dining room. Yes, it is true that the lady had the higher rank! As the end of 3609 drew nigh its demise was marked by a letter to The Times which was published on 17th December1960.

FIGHTER CONTROL
Sir - On Friday, December 9th, in a written Parliamentary answer, the Secretary of State for Air announced the disbandment of the remaining fighter control units of the Royal Auxiliary Air Force. Formed soon after the war, they have until now been an integral, though unpublicized, part of the early warning radar defences of this country. The thousands of spare-time officers, airmen and air-women who have served therein over the last 12 or 13 years reached a fantastically high standard of operational effectiveness vis-à-vis their regular colleagues: their record of attendance was unequalled by any other reserve force: and throughout the cold war to date they have been a real part of the defensive complement to the deterrent. Now, unobtrusively, they are to be disbanded and the air force will have lost both a source of strength and yet another link with the civilian environment on which it must rely.

I may not comment on the manner of their disbandment. If it is a fact that their use is now limited, as they could not be called out in time of emergency without the medieval trappings of a royal proclamation, they must go. It is also a fact that the units were never advised that this was a difficulty, nor invited to offer suggestions to get round it. Neither were their Territorial and Auxiliary Forces Associations consulted. If the Royal Air Force does not require their manpower, they must go. But the Air Ministry will no doubt be cautious in future appeals for more men and women for static employment.

Some day the wheel of policy may turn, and a real need for a reserve force be envisaged. Despite their dismissal, even while still being promised a real future of service, the old auxiliaries may return. But a fund of goodwill and loyal service may have been dissipated.

I am, Sir, your obedient servant

W.A. BEAUMONT, Wing Commander, Officer Commanding 3609 (West Riding) Fighter Control unit, Royal Auxiliary Air Force, Wheatfield, Wood Lane, Headingley, Leeds 6.

It was a sad end for the many patriotic men and women who came from far and wide in the county to enjoy the esprit de corps. Typical amongst them was Corporal Peter Brown, demobbed in 1946, who volunteered for the auxiliary squadron at Yeadon the following year.

His service with 609 and 3609 embraced the change-over from piston to jet engines before moving on to the complex radar equipment. Corporal Desmond Park recalled the friendly atmosphere, with everyone on Christian name terms, and ranks were only strictly adhered to during visits to active service stations. In fact, in many cases, roles were reversed when back at work on Monday mornings. Peter Brown remembers Wheatfield as a lively place on Saturday nights with around 100 people present, and aptly described it as 'a centre of happy times.' After the Saturday dance or social, the teams who were going on to the coast next morning slept in segregated quarters upstairs with 'no corridor creeping allowed.' Marcia Clark joined 3609 as a trainee 'Fighter Plotter' in 1951 for six years extensive training and recalls the very enjoyable social side. On Saturday evenings she would help transport big trays of meat and potato pies from a cafe in Bradford. Her fondest recollection however was when ex Polish paratrooper Bruno Mroz told her he would like to drink champagne from her shoe, and immensely flattered, she allowed him to try, forgetting she had 'peep-toe' shoes on and it went all over the place!

All squadron members received a letter on Ist January 1961 from Wing Commander W.A. Beaumont asking them to report on Sunday, 8th January at 10am (best blue, no medals), to thank them all officially for their magnificent service and outlining arrangements for a final parade on 28th January.

After lying dormant for a time, Wheatfield, together with two other centres, North Leeds (now the site of Potternewton Sports Centre) and South Leeds (the former Workhouse in Domestic Street), became training centres for the Mentally Handicapped under Leeds City Council Social Services. Part of Wheatfield House, two annexe blocks and some prefabricated wartime buildings were used by about 12 members of staff acting as instructors to the 80-100 students, who when split into small groups were taught basic skills to improve their lives, with simple training in cooking and domestic science, sewing, dressmaking, art and woodwork etc. Ages varied from 16 years to retirement and many continued to attend beyond that. Their disabilities covered a wide range, from learning difficulties, Down's Syndrome, epilepsy, mental breakdowns and severe physical handicaps. They attended from 9am to 4pm, most being bussed from surrounding areas. A basic education programme was provided - literacy, numeracy and social awareness and the instructors took groups swimming and on supervised holidays.

To help towards financing these projects, simple repetitive contract work was also undertaken which enabled those attending to be paid a small wage. Mr. Leslie Birch, one of the instructors, recalled some of the monotonous jobs undertaken, anything that could not be carried out by a machine, such as folding up boxes or various packing jobs, and the woodwork side was developed to produce simple garden furniture. Fred Ward, another man heavily involved with the centres, also recalls a thriving printing department where letterheads, tickets, handbills, etc. were produced and the assembly of telephone junction boxes was undertaken.

The schools only closed in 1976 when four new purpose-built centres were introduced at Ramshead Wood, Seacroft, and in Bramley, Middleton and Wetherby. A freezer centre established for the preparation of school dinners for local schools continued in the coach house for many more years, but by now, the old house was crying out for some tender loving care, and its finest hour was just around the corner!

The house as it looked in 1976 when aquired by the Sue Ryder Care Foundation for £40,000, the conservatory being replaced by a simple corrugated awning.

Early in 1975 Mrs Kathleen Merryweather A.M.I.S.W., the Principal Social Worker at St. James's Hospital, Leeds, was chairing one of the regular Social Work Department meetings when problems arising from the lack of a Leeds Hospice came up for discussion yet again. This meeting was to be the catalyst which started a three year chain reaction resulting in the formation of the first Leeds Hospice.

Manorlands at Oxenhope in the Worth Valley, and the Marie Curie Home in Ilkley were providing excellent service in a caring environment, but their locations, well out of Leeds, caused problems of separation for relatives and friends of patients at the very time when contact was of prime importance. At the next meeting of the Leeds Hospital Chaplains at St. James's Hospital, chaired by the resident chaplain, The Rev. Hector Huxham, Mrs. Merryweather was invited to join them for lunch before the afternoon meeting in the Post Graduate Suite. She shared with the chaplains the Social Workers' concerns about the lack of a hospice in the city. At the discussions that followed it was agreed that a busy hospital ward was not the best place for dying patients, and their families.

The driving force behind the creation of Wheatfields Hospice -Dr. Douglas B. MacAdam, M.A., B.D., M.B., M.R.C.G.P.

It was at this time that a man of vision, with boundless enthusiasm and energy came to the fore - the Reverend Dr. Douglas MacAdam, M.A., B.D.M.B., M.R.C.G.P. He was a full-time lecturer in General Practice, in the Department of Community Medicine at Leeds University, a doctor, doing his clinical work at Meanwood Health Centre, and an Associate Minister at Headingley Hill United Reformed Church. In addition to all these commitments, he was also a member of the Institute of Religion and Medicine, and at a meeting of the Institute on 25th April 1975, members discussed the steps required to create a Hospice for the city.

The first stage was the formation of a steering committee to plan a course of action. In addition to medical and nursing interests, membership of the committee reflected the concern of the community in general for the professional care of patients with chronic and terminal diseases. On the initial committee were Kathleen Merryweather; Mr. Arthur C. Tillotson, who became Treasurer; Mary Stratton, M.B.E., B.A. as Secretary, who had a wealth of experience and knowledge from her work with the Leeds Council for Voluntary Service; Professor Charles A Joslin, B.S. F.R.C.R., D.M.R.T., C.ENG, from Cookridge Hospital who brought to the team valuable knowledge gained from the setting up of the Bradford Hospice, Manorlands, under the Sue Ryder Foundation; Mr James Ashcroft, Architect; Dr Douglas MacAdam, Chairperson; Dr Reg Lunton F.R.E.P, consultant Physician and recently retired from hospice work at St Ann's, Manchester.

The Steering Committee had their first meeting on 11th June 1975, followed by visits to a number of hospices including St Christopher's Hospice, London and St Anne's Hospice, Manchester and homes showing the work of the Sue Ryder Foundation. All this activity led to probably the most significant meeting in the development of the Leeds Hospice project on 10th February 1976, when the founder of the Sue Ryder Foundation, Lady Ryder of Warsaw C.M.G., O.B.E. met the Steering Committee.

At about this time, during the discussions with the Sue Ryder Foundation and just before our appeal went public, the Steering Committee was approached for the first time by representatives of the proposed St Gemma's Hospice. We were told that St Gemma's Convent was to be the site of a purpose built Hospice with the backing of the Congregation of the Convent Sisters and the Roman Catholic Church authorities. The project was assured of finance and the Steering Committee was invited to drop its project with the Sue Ryder Foundation and join with St Gemma's. Despite the attractiveness of the offer, the Committee were resolved to provide a hospice representing the multi-denominational, multi-faith and secular people of Leeds and district. Spiritual values were seen as an essential part of caring for the dying but the Hospice needed to be accountable to the citizens of Leeds and to make its appeal irrespective of religious affiliation. It was decided to proceed with our work independently and to co-operate with the planned St Gemma's Hospice in all practical ways.

Therefore, after much discussion they resolved to work towards the establishment of a new hospice, quoted in the Yorkshire Evening Post as 'The Leeds Hospice for Continuing Care'. The whole project was to be self financed by a Public Appeal once a suitable building could be found. The other resolution carried, after some reservations, was that the Leeds Committee should be known as 'The Leeds Team of the Sue Ryder Foundation' and the Hospice would become a Sue Ryder Home - very appropriate as Sue Ryder was a 'local lass' born at Scarcroft Grange near Leeds, in 1923. Her father, Charles, was a director of the famous Joshua Tetley Brewery in Leeds.

The next step was for Dr. MacAdam to approach Leeds City Council for a suitable building or site for the project. They were very supportive, and offered several premises for inspection, most of which were visited by the Doctor and Mrs. Merryweather, including a large house in Whitkirk, a site in Halton, and even a school, but it was Wheatfield, the old listed house in Headingley, which fitted the bill. It was agreed that this house would be available on the 8th June 1976, but the Committee could not take over until later in the year when the Social Services were scheduled to move out. The Sue Ryder Foundation was duly invoiced for the sum of £40,000 for this run down old house.

The Yorkshire Evening Post of 8th January 1977 reported on a meeting of the previous evening at the Civic Hall under the headline:
COME ON! HELP THE £100,000 WAR AGAINST PAIN

The Lord Mayor, Councillor Ernest Morris, presided over the meeting where the two speakers were Miss Sue Ryder and Dr. T. S. West from St. Christopher's Hospice in London. Dr. West showed slides of the London Hospice and described part of their work as 'teasing out components of pain - be it physical, mental, social or spiritual - and treating them'. Dr. MacAdam, Chairman of the Organising Committee, talked about the project and the launching of the £100,000 Evening Post backed appeal to convert Wheatfields (which had now been made plural) into a hospice to take up to 30 patients and, subject to public response, he hoped the first patients would be admitted before the end of the year. The report ended, as did all weekly press notices, with Treasurer, Mr. Arthur Tillotson's address in Bardsey, and from now on it was all systems go!

Doubts are often cast on the efficiency of large committees and their inevitable difficulties in making decisions and actually getting things done, but the first Wheatfields Organising Committee was certainly a large winning team. It consisted of nineteen members, and cut across all political and religious boundaries. They set about the task of raising money for converting the building and equipping and staffing the hospice with boundless energy.

The full Committee, and their qualifications, were as follows :
CHAIRMAN: Revd. Dr. D. B. MacAdam M.A., B.D., MB., M.R.C.G.P.
HON. SECRETARY: Miss B. M. Stratton, M.B.E., B.A.
HON. TREASURER: Mr. A. C. Tillotson
HON. SECRETARY OF FRIENDS OF WHEATFIELDS: Rev. P. Clarke, M.A.
(Hospital Chaplain and Labour City Councillor)
Mr. D. Aspinall (Builder)
Mr. J. H. Ashcroft, B. Arch (L'pool), R.I.B.A., F.I.Arb.
Mr. H. Brown
Revd. Canon R. G. G. Foley, B.A. (Durh), Vicar of Leeds
Dr. W. J. Green, M.B., Ch.B., M.F.C.M. Medical Officer for Health
Professor C. A. Joslin, B.S., F.R.C.R., D.M.R.T., C.Eng
R. W. Luxton, M.D., B.Sc., F.R.C.P. (Lond).
Cllr. W. Merritt, S.R.N., R.M.N.
Mrs. K. Merryweather, A.I.M.S.W.
Revd. G. Spelman, Chaplain of T.A.S.C., for Bishop of Leeds
Mr. R. Stacey, F.C.A., Leeds Rotary Club
Mr J Tyler, retired Hospital Supplies Officer
Miss M. Walton, S.R.N., S.C.M., H.V. Cert., City Health Dept. (Nursing)
Cllr. Mrs. M. White, Conservative City Councillor

and they could call on the support of the following 35 local patrons :

Peter Alliss	S.A.Barr
St. John Binns	K.O. Boardman
Professor A. J. Brown	Rabbi Dr. S. Brown
N. B. Capindale	S. Cope
Miss A. M. Eldon	F. R. Evans
Professor J. C. Goligher	Brigadier K. Hargreaves
E. Hayhurst	Professor D. R. Wood

Denis Healey	J. Hiley
Sir Keith Joseph	Bishop of Leeds
Baroness Masham	Professor G. P. McNicol
Moderator of the Leeds	Lord Normanby
Free Church Federal Council	Dr. P. J. Nuttgens
Bishop of Wakefield	Lady Tunbridge

The Committee lost no time in circulating an appeal 'flyer' under the title:-
'Wheatfields - A Home for Continuing Care'
for WAKEFIELD, LEEDS & KIRKLEES, which set out its aims as follows:-

WHEATFIELDS
Wood Lane, Headingley, Leeds, LS6 2AE
OUR PURPOSE IS TO PROVIDE CONTINUING CARE FOR PATIENTS WITH
ADVANCED DISEASE - MANY WITH CANCER.
A large number of patients dying from cancer suffer unnecessarily. Our hospitals are
primarily designed to diagnose and treat disease. When patients have received all the
treatment that can be given by a modern hospital they still require help getting back to
life. When nothing more can be done for the disease, much can still be done for the patient.

WHY IS A HOME SUCH AS WHEATFIELDS NECESSARY?
Although many cancer patients can be cured, sometimes this is not possible. With
medical and nursing skills it is always possible to continue caring. Many of us have
had friends or relatives whom we could have helped in the last few weeks of life if
only there had been a suitable home where there was nursing and medical care. This
requires a special home - where friends and relatives are always welcome, where
spiritual values are clearly recognised, and where there will be peace, cheerfulness
and dignity.

WHY ARE THESE PATIENTS NOT NURSED IN A HOSPITAL?
Some of them are, but beds are not always available when most needed, and priority
is given to those who would benefit from curative treatment and to emergencies. A
busy hospital ward is not the best place for a dying person who needs peace and an
extremely flexible nursing routine. Wheatfields will be a home complementary to the
Hospital Service, accepting patients from a population of 2 million in parts of
Yorkshire, Leeds, Wakefield and Kirklees.

HOW GREAT IS THE NEED?
In a population the size of ours there are around 3,000 deaths from cancer a year.
Studies in other parts of the country have shown that there is severe difficulty and

discomfort during the last two weeks of life in more than 25% of those dying from cancer, whether at home or in an acute hospital. This suffering can be avoided with skill and care. At least 600 people a year in this area need the care of a Home such as Wheatfields.

WHAT IS BEING DONE?
The Home at Wheatfields has been acquired. Conversion work is in hand. The main structural alterations involve the installation of a hydraulic lift, a first floor extension for toilets, bathroom and sluices, and the addition of a ground floor sitting room.
Built as a home in the 1850s, extended in the 1890s in Venetian style, it was used as a family residence until the outbreak of war. In the 1970s Wheatfields will now become a home again, offering a special service to the patients who need very loving care.

AT LEAST £100,000 IS REQUIRED TO PAY FOR THE CONVERSION
The running costs will inevitably be high as professional staff will be paid appropriately; qualified nursing staff will be in constant attendance over the 24 hours of the day, in addition to the other staff.

HOW CAN YOU HELP?
• Your help in continuing this Appeal to raise money.
• Your help by becoming a Friend of Wheatfields - even if you do not send a donation, please return the attached slip so that you can receive more information.
• Your prayers.
Wheatfields is for those who are in greatest need; patients and relatives will contribute as they are able.

This will help Wheatfields to be a very special home – providing continuing, expert, sympathetic and personal nursing care for those whose need is so great and who will be so grateful.

Donations flowed in at a steady rate and the first of many fund raising events, continuing to this day, got underway. Countless coffee mornings, cheese and wine parties, concerts, bed pushes, bring and buy sales, raffles, and even a Caribbean Evening at Debenham's Briggate store. Lord Normandy made a very significant donation at a particularly difficult time which helped give confidence that the project would not fade or fail.

One of the first events was a Ploughman's Lunch on Friday 18th March 1976 organised by the Social Work Department at St James's Hospital, from 12 noon to 2.00 p.m., good value at 50p a ticket! Several members asked 'what is Wheatfields?' and soon found out when Dr. MacAdam climbed on to a plastic chair and told them of his plans and ideas.

Two weeks into the Appeal £17,763 had been raised, and by mid February £22,933 rising to £25,335 early in March. To promote the project, Wheatfields House was opened to the public on 30th March, and from 10.00 a.m. to noon, and 2.00 p.m. to 4.00 p.m. no less than 600 visitors took advantage of the open invitation and enjoyed refreshments supplied by the 1830 group of St.Michael's Church, Headingley. The Yorkshire Evening Post of 8th April reported the Treasurer acknowledging over £250 being raised from the first Wheatfields Flag Day, giving a total fund of £34,540. At the same time all interested supporters were invited to contact the Secretary of 'The Friends of Wheatfields', the Rev. Phillip Clarke, Chaplain at Leeds Infirmary. Offers of help towards the Hospice venture and the formation of support Groups were soon being co-ordinated by the 'Friends' Chairman, Mr. Murray Japp, who was closely involved with the Hospice for the next two decades, including holding the position of Chairman of the House Committee.

Support came from well outside the Leeds area, including Wakefield, Pontefract, Harrogate, York and Huddersfield. All these places created their own Hospices eventually, but they gave considerable support to the Leeds project as well as creating useful publicity for the whole Hospice movement.

Wheatfields came into the hands of the Sue Ryder Foundation on 31st March 1977 by which time the fund was almost halfway towards its £100,000 target, and the first workmen moved in. The Committee was once again fortunate in securing the services of a small well qualified team to supervise and organise the work, much of which was carried out by personnel from Manpower Services under the Government's Job Creation Scheme, who not only provided the workers but paid them a basic wage during their time on site, and teams of volunteers worked alongside, particularly at weekends.

The Architect responsible for this massive task was Mr. Nigel Merryweather, M.A. R.I.B.A. (Kathleen's son) who had to manage on a Job Creation allowance of £50 per week. Mr. Dennis Aspinall, a retired builder, became a volunteer Clerk of Works, with Ken Tindall acting as volunteer foreman.

Another talented volunteer who came to the fore was John Tyler, a man with experience of running a hospital supplies department. This dedicated small team established its headquarters in the first room to the right of the front door. This room, once Joseph Nicholson's study, was, and still is, quite different from the rest of the house. It had escaped the rebuilding of the house in the 1880s and eventually became the Hospice chapel, a haven of peace for patients and staff during periods of stress. Rex Stacey of Leeds Rotary Club and other Rotarians gave practical support and assistance.

Further fundraising followed, with A4 posters being circulated asking for help with building materials - with current high prices it is well worth recording the works list and estimated values in 1977: 300 dressed stones £1.50 each, 6000 bricks at 4p each, 5 loads of sand at £15 a load, 30 doors at £15 each, 100 bags of cement at £1.20 a bag, 500 bathroom tiles at 5p each, 5 steel beams at £50 each, 600 pieces of timber at £10 each, and 2000 concrete blocks at 15p each.

Round Table volunteers clearing the site of ex-wartime buildings in Spring 1977. This area is now mainly most attractive gardens to the front of the house.

The first major jobs were the demolition of some of the wartime structures, the unsightly prefabricated buildings along the left hand wall side being dismantled and removed by members of the Calverley and Headingley Round Table. Removing the concrete construction to the left of what is now the annexe was a far more serious problem, and to reduce this to a pile of rubble capable of being moved by a bulldozer took many days of noisy pneumatic drilling. The effort and cost required in this demolition work ensured that the main annexe block with its heavy concrete roof was to be retained - a blessing in disguise, as it provided much needed administrative office space, and in time became the headquarters of the Hospice fundraising activities.

The College of Building, Leeds Polytechnic, and the Construction Industry Training Board all came forward with professional advice and provided students to assist in

THE SUE RYDER FOUNDATION

WHEATFIELDS

~ A Home for Continuing Care ~

WOOD LANE · HEADINGLEY · LEEDS 6

Help us to finance the adaptation of the house for our use as a Home:

	each
300 dressed stones	£1·50
6000 bricks	4p
5 loads of sand	15·00
30 doors	15·00
100 bags cement	1·20
500 bathroom tiles	5p
5 steel beams	50·00
600 pieces of timber	10·00
2000 concrete blocks	15p

Typical early fundraising poster of the 1977 period. Would that it was still possible to purchase 30 doors for £15, even then rather optimistic!

appropriate areas of work. Inevitably certain specialised tasks, such as electrical work, central heating, and the surfacing of the new drive had to be contracted out, and the September installation of the hydraulic lift, costing £18,000, in the prepared shaft built up from the basement to the first floor.

Apart from the building of the lift shaft, one of the other major construction jobs was the addition of a sitting room to the left hand side of the façade. This new room was entered via double doors from what had been the drawing room of the house, and was to become the patients, and staff dining room in the early years of the Hospice. The whole of this new extension was on the site of the conservatory/palm house, which had been demolished just after the war and subsequently replaced with a rather austere carport type of structure.

Most of the time, this mixture of professional and casual workers and volunteers worked well, but with all the ever changing job creation personnel being drafted in, there would have to be a rotten apple or two at the bottom of the barrel! It was fortunate that Nigel Merryweather called in on his way home late one evening to find that a team of young day workers had returned to strip the lead from the roof!!

The grounds of the house were to present a major challenge, and it was indeed fortunate that Alan Smith, of the then Leeds Polytechnic Department of Landscape Architecture, made this a project for his students. Many plans and ideas were submitted before a winning layout was chosen, and Alan Smith's abundant experience came to the fore with his original planting incorporating 250 shrubs and 20 climbing plants, intended to give a fine all year round visual display with 10 conifers and 20 other trees, as well as providing various seats for visitors and patients.

Landscaping started with the back-breaking task of removing the builders' rubble and general rubbish about the site. Much of this was carried out over a 10 day Easter Holiday, with the inevitable April showers, by 13 dedicated young people, directed by Alan Smith and Bob Ingle who also gave up their holiday. A team of young Quakers came when the project was chosen as one of the Quaker Work Camps for the year, and when they left they were confident the first fruits of their labours would be apparent by midsummer.

Another team who did valuable work was a dozen first year students from Jacob Kramer College, who worked on the redecoration of the main ground floor rooms over a period of 6 weeks as part of their 28 week Construction Industry training course. Thankfully the college was allowed a special dispensation to enable them to assist Registered Charities with similar projects providing all the decorating materials were provided by the recipients. All the work was supervised by Maurice Fray, the Head of the Painting and Decorating Department, who recalls the skilled work required, particularly in repairing the elaborate plasterwork cornices over the staircase, and the horror experienced one morning when the team found someone had put a foot through one of the ceilings! In the end, the results were so good they were asked to return some four years later to redecorate two main rooms.

Soon, key staff positions would have to be filled, and the first appointment was that of Matron in March 1978, when Miss Maire O'Donnell, S.R.N., O.N.C., aged 36, whose youthful looks belied her 20 years wealth of nursing experience, arrived. Born in Keighley, educated at St. Joseph's College, Bradford, she followed that with a short 6 month career in a market garden before enrolling as a student nurse at Woodlands Orthopaedic Hospital, going on to qualify as an S.R.N. at the Dreadnought Seaman's Hospital, Greenwich. After more nursing experience in Gloucestershire, she offered her services for voluntary work overseas which led her to a Catholic Leprosy Hospital in Guyana.

The first Matron of the Hospice Miss Maire O'Donnell, S.R.N., O.N.C., appointed in March 1978, who went on to give 15 years of dedicated service.

On returning to England she was appointed as Sister at Airedale Hospital, but to gain more experience she became a 'House Mother' at Cowgill House, the Leeds Catholic Children's Society Home in Bramley. Her last post was as an Assistant Matron at Manorlands, the Bradford Sue Ryder Hospice at Oxenhope. It would be difficult to think of anyone more fitted for the post of Matron at Wheatfields, where she gave 15 years devoted service to the Hospice.

On 10th March, the local papers carried the news that the Honorary Clinical Director for the new Hospice would be Dr. David J. Charley, O.B.E., F.R.C.P., Consultant Physician at Leeds Chest Clinic and Killingbeck Hospital, who was aptly described by the Yorkshire Evening Post reporter, Barrie Farnill, as a 'lively and friendly 59 year old'. He was personally well qualified, as apart from his extensive medical experience, he held the position of

Deacon of the Baptist Church. A deeply committed Christian, with four grown up children, his wife Joan had tragically died from cancer the previous November.

Dr. Charley had been approached at home in Shaw Lane early in 1978 by Dr. MacAdam, and asked if he would consider becoming the first Medical Director of the proposed Hospice, with the proviso that there would be no pay! Needless to say, he accepted, and three years later when he retired from the National Health Service he was able to devote all his time to Wheatfields, from which time the Hospice paid his Medical Insurance premium until he finally retired.

Saturday, 3rd June 1978 - The first open day. It's hard to believe but on this day 1,200 people came to tour the house with members of the House Committee, and £253 was raised for the funds.

For the first few years he was to rely heavily on the voluntary support of his local medical colleagues.

By Spring the tempo at Wheatfields was gaining momentum as the race was on for the Hospice to open in Summer 1978!

CHAPTER 7
WHEATFIELDS HOSPICE -
THE DREAM BECOMES REALITY

On 14th April 1978 the Treasurer's weekly press report recorded that the Wheatfield Fund had passed the initial target of £100,000, following a generous donation of £1,500 by Leeds Rotary Club. The citizens of Leeds had certainly taken the Hospice project to their hearts, but inevitably, more money had to be found if the equipping of the house was to be completed within a reasonable time. The revised target called for an additional £35,000 which was given a kick-start of £4,000 raised in a hastily arranged flag day the following week.

Soon it was time to equip and furnish the bedrooms, lounge and dining areas, a lot of expensive equipment being involved, the cost of which was to have a considerable bearing on the number of patients who could be accommodated.

An early layout drawing shows proposals for 9 beds on the ground floor and 17 more on the first floor. This very ambitious forecast was finally reduced to a modest 9 bed ground floor layout and a staffing level to suit this more realistic intake was the first priority.

The committee recognised from the start that 90% of caring for the terminally ill was the work of nurses, and that only the highest quality nursing was acceptable for palliative care. For 9 patients, this equated to a staff of 14, made up of 4 sisters, 2 staff nurses, 4 state controlled nurses and 4 nursing auxiliaries, all to be employed at current National Health rates. Dr. Charley recalls the permanent staff were augmented by a considerable number of volunteer nurses who offered regular sessions at weekends. Several of these volunteers were senior administrative staff from the National Health Service who were glad to leave their desks and get back to some real nursing. Jewish nurses offered to cover on Christmas Day and thankfully, there was no shortage of people wanting to 'share the care'.

From the start the doctors and nurses recognised that this was acute nursing, the opposite of 'elderly' care, as patients' conditions are constantly changing and in need of close monitoring. Nobody could say 'I got it right' with regard to pain control, as what was right today might be wrong tomorrow. They had to be constantly on the look-out for other non-cancerous conditions, as a patient dying of cancer can still have an appendicitis, gastric ulcer problems or painful toothache, all in need of emergency treatment.

A number of G.P.s and other practising doctors volunteered their time one day a week, when they were 'on call' for 24 hours, doing a round of all the patients during that day and being available for admissions and emergencies. They would also do one weekend in six, and there was never a lack of volunteers!

Many Consultants offered their skills and expertise when requested, the Hospice being particularly indebted to the oncologists from Cookridge Hospital and the anaesthetists specialising in pain control. (Pain Control clinics were still a thing of the future.)

The Hospice movement well and truly established the value and position of volunteer help - now far more widely accepted. In June 1978, the Committee appointed Mrs. Laura Hampton as Organiser of Voluntary Helpers, with responsibility for appointing the first of an army of volunteers to assist the nursing staff, as well as the administrative and secretarial personnel, along with teams to assist with the maintenance of the house and gardens.

Another essential task was the expansion of fundraising activities to introduce new ideas and major events, encourage the development and formation of support groups, and to assist many active individual fundraisers. One solo fundraiser from the early days was the one and only Lucy Boulton, who as well as offering hands-on voluntary work, in the first 18 months of the Hospice. She personally raised almost £2,000. An active Christian, Lucy was a member of the local St. Chad's Parish Church Mothers Union, served on the Management Committee of the Leeds Old People's Welfare

Council, and was well known for saying, 'I like being involved', and putting forward her forthright views, such as, 'I'm concerned, I want people to be more caring and sharing and loving. It isn't what you have, it's what you do with it.' No wonder that very few people over the years passed her Tombola stand at the Garden Party without parting with money!

The sales teams of volunteers have one of the hardest jobs in fundraising - lifting, carrying, sorting and selling large quantities of donated goods. Supervision of clothing sales in the early years was by Mrs. Audrey Hockney, an ex A.T.S. sergeant whose bark at times could be far worse than her bite, and she developed the sales side in five years from earning about £5 per week to £10,000 a year. Mrs. Maureen Bray, a volunteer since 1979, finally took over. Long service is a tradition amongst fundraising volunteers. Typical of this is school teacher Michael Bourne who since Christmas 1980 has been responsible for valuing and organising the sale of donated books. From an insignificant start from the tops of tea trolleys, book sales have raised well over £85,000 in 20 years, a tribute to the long serving team of book lovers who manned the book stalls at Hospice sales and book fairs all over the area. Michael is famous for his dry sense of humour and when he can't move for books in the store, says the worst words you can hear from a customer is 'I'll bring it back when I've read it!'

Ros Jenkins spotted another potential winner with the sale of bric-a-brac which had initially been sold in a small way from boxes in the garage, when she invited Marie Turner, an office volunteer, to organise a team, which developed into a major fundraising exercise which still draws crowds of customers on Friday mornings and Tuesday afternoons.

To comply with the Constitution of the Sue Ryder Foundation, on 1st June 1978, the original steering committee responsible for the creation of Wheatfields was disbanded to be replaced by the first House Committee. This management team chaired by Dr. MacAdam was to consist of three officers, ten members drawn from the Leeds area and two representatives of the Foundation.

The next two months were amongst the most exciting at the old house, as the ground floor neared completion, and on Saturday, 3rd June 1978, from 10am to 5pm, visitors were welcomed to tour the house. Yorkshire folk had raised the money to make the project possible, and now they were about to see how the 'brass' had been spent, all 1,200 of them! The Friends of Wheatfields manned what must have been a very busy refreshment stall, a bring-and-buy sale on the day raised £253 and members of the House Committee gave conducted tours of the ground floor. The only cloud on the horizon was the Treasurer's report that £500 of lead had been stolen from the roof, which sadly cost more money which had to be raised, but the fund had now risen to £111,614.

It was about this time that the first nursing staff as well as catering and domestic personnel were being appointed. The two nursing sisters were Joyce Simm and Barbara Farish along with nurses Angela Hughes, Ursula O'Keef and Mary Murphy, the latter being the only original member of staff still at the Hospice. Mary was wanting to return to nursing as her daughter neared school age, but one of her first duties was far from normal work. She fondly recalls the nights when pairs of nurses took turns on the rota of night watchmen shifts, sleeping in the old dining room, while Dr. Charley had a sleeping bag in the new Hospice kitchen. There was no more lead or valuable equipment stolen with this home-grown security system in place.

On 21st June 1978, the Hospice was formally opened by Jimmy Savile O.B.E., in the presence of the Lord Mayor of Leeds, Councillor Harry Booth, along with Sue Ryder and invited guests. Jimmy Savile, photographed by the Yorkshire Evening Post in characteristic pose, his long white hair topped with a large tin bowl, and wearing large orange framed sunglasses, sporting a huge cigar, was quoted as saying 'We are all very lucky to be standing here. This is not going to be a sad, quiet place, it's going to be one of fun and happiness', and promised his support in the future. Dr. MacAdam thanked all the people and organisations which had made the Hospice possible, and reported that over 4,000 individuals and groups had answered the Wheatfields Appeal and helped to raise £130,000. In his best Churchillian mode he pointed out, 'This is just the beginning, not the end. We need a lot more to finish the capital appeal, but after that we need continued support if the Hospice will eventually look after 600 people a year.'

On Sunday, 2nd July, 1978 at 4 p.m. the Bishop of Ripon, the Rt. Revd. David Young, M.A. led an Ecumenical Service in the Home and dedicated the Chapel, the first room on the right on entering the Hospice.

Last minute building work was all that remained to be completed to totally satisfy the inspection by the Fire Officers. It was quite a relief when the magnificent mahogany doors offered adequate fire-resistance, and a joy to hear 'You are all clear to open.' Matron could now ring round offering places to patients.

On Thursday, 18th August, the first patient arrived, Mr. Fred Brooks of Otley, who was pictured with one of the nurses in a main article in the Yorkshire Evening Post under the banner headline 'WE'VE MADE IT! WHEATFIELDS - THE E.P.

BACKED HOSPICE – SOARS PAST ITS £135,000 TARGET.'

By the end of the year when the House Committee tendered its first Annual Report, the hospice had cared for 41 patients (21 male and 20 female), with an average length of stay of 32.8 days, their ages ranging from 40 to 86 years! The report recorded that all the initial building work on site was completed, the annexe building was now in use for administration and benefits to patients were continually improving with offers of specialist help, physiotherapy, occupational therapy, a chiropodist and a most welcome hairdresser.

By this time, the nursing staff had grown to 50 full and part time staff and 118 new volunteers were offering four hours voluntary work per week.

June 1979 saw the introduction of a regular Friday coffee morning, a popular feature still continuing today. Another volunteer success story was the gardens which were becoming a setting worthy of the caring concern of the Hospice.

Saturday, the 21st July 1979 was the date selected for the first Garden Party, which over the years became one of the most popular fundraising events. In September of that year the Hospice's new Publicity and Appeals Assistant, Sylvia Longstaff introduced the first of the highly successful annual long distance sponsored walks, which became very popular and remain so to this day. The taxing 42 miles of the North York Moors - Lyke Wake Route attracted 249 people who raised £8,000. For 1980 it was the challenge of the Three Peaks, Whernside, Ingleborough and Penyghent, which raised £10,000.

Over the years new 12 hour walks generally in the 25 mile range were introduced in some of the most attractive parts of the Yorkshire Dales, which raised incredible sums of money thanks to the walk organisers and their teams of expert volunteers. One of the first to assist was Walter Smith who went on to give countless hours of dedicated support to walkers over the years.

One sad note in the summer of 1980 was the departure for a new post in Perth, Western Australia, of the Chairman Douglas MacAdam, whose vision and leadership surely made Wheatfields such a success story. He left behind him a 22 bed unit taking care of over 300 patients and their families each year. The City of Leeds will never know just how much it owes to this one man!

His position as Chairman of the House Committee was taken by his deputy, David H. Wilson, F.R.C.S., a Consultant Surgeon at Leeds General Infirmary, who was not to know that storm clouds were building up on the horizon.

By early 1981 the Hospice was making headlines in the local paper again, but for all the wrong reasons. Under the heading, WHEATFIELDS AT CROSSROADS IN CASH CRISIS, it was revealed that it now cost £250,000 a year to maintain the high standards of the Hospice and that they had just carried over a debt of £60,000.

Colin Welland, the Yorkshire author, playwright and actor took up the challenge to promote Wheatfields, and the doom and gloom started to lift. He had first hand experience of the Hospice when it had looked after his father-in-law. Colin went on to launch a massive appeal at the Astoria Ballroom alongside Chairman David Wilson with a target of £125,000 to be raised in a year and leading to the popular 'Share the Care' form of fundraising when money is raised to sponsor a bed, at that time running at £36 per day.

Yorkshire playwright and author Colin Welland launching the £125,000 appeal to rescue Wheatfields from its cash crisis on Thursday, 4th May, 1981, at the Astoria Ballroom, Leeds, with the slogan 'Share the Care at Wheatfields'. To the left of the photograph is David Wildon, Chairman of the House Committee and Howard Davies, Publicity Consultant and a prominent member of the House Committee for many years.

By the end of the year a £25,000 grant from the Leeds Area Hospital Authority and a spate of generous donations and fundraising meant the crisis was avoided.

Colin Welland backed up his appeal for money by taking part in that year's 30 mile sponsored walk, The Bilsdale Circuit, where he joined 428 walkers who collectively raised some £15,000. Later, penning his impressions of the experience in the Autumn issue of the Hospice news letter 'The Link', under the heading COLIN'S GREAT

In 1981 Dr. David J. Charley, the very popular first Honorary Medical Director received a cheque for £3,600 following a sponsored swim by pupils of Richmond House and Far Headingley Preparatory School. No-one could have forecast the result of their endeavours, as almost every child from 6 to 11 years in the school took part, even those who could only just manage to get a foot off the floor of the bath. They were the ones who were sponsored by the stroke and not by the length! All who took part found it great fun as well as a very worthwhile event, and these young people are an example to us all.

FEET, he wrote as follows: "I knew, as soon as I'd stepped out of the car, that I'd made a mistake. There was a vigour in the air, the like of which I'd not been a part of for twenty years. A bright mist had settled on the slopes around me - comforting - reassuring - perhaps they'd call the whole thing off.

"But I should have recognised in the light eager chatter which pierced the fog - the clusters of bubbling anoraks, green, blue, scarlet (Oh for the odd streak of yellow) and the ruddy health food countenances - that all thoughts of surrender were solely mine. The rest were on Task Force tenterhooks to set about their business, lining up, for the numbers which would release them from their leashes and send them bounding up and away into the (Blast it) rapidly lifting gloom.

"The first three miles were Hell - absolute Hell. Up an almost vertical ascent of several hundred feet and then along a roller-coaster of lung-wrenching ups and knee-rending downs. There was, of course, an easy way, round the foot of the ridge quite above board, quite legitimate, which none of the SAS around me chose to tell me about .... the swines.

"I scrambled, whimpering up an Eiger face, clinging to my wife's rucksack ahead (bless her), dreaming only of Blighty, as two elderly ladies, immediately behind, blithely discussed the state of Harrogate shops and shopping.

"What else I don't know - I go deaf when I'm exhausted - but as they passed my floundering form they smiled and shared the view with me … as I go blind, as well, it seemed a waste of effort.

"The four-mile checkpoint appeared like Alex of the 'Ice Cold' fame. Tea, hot tea, always very good for shock, proved to be the ultimate deceiver. Its warm sustenance coursing through the marrow of my protesting limbs persuaded them to go on - to chance it - to leave the tents, the urn, the minibus, the cosy chatter of boy scouts behind, and tread where millions of men, women and children had trod before ... but not me.

"After six more miles of sticky bog, delirium began to set in. The last elderly walker had long since passed - vultures were circling overhead - coyotes lurked in the heather either side. Soldiers chuckled into their intercoms as this decrepit heap lurched past - my wife smiling apologetically for having anything to do with me. I began to gibber...!

"Then - a shout! Way across the landscape of the moon, many, many leagues away, stood a cluster of anxious figures. By now my hearing had begun to fail but I just about made out my name. 'Where the hell have you been?' they asked.

"I could have told them where I'd been. I'd been to the mouth of hell and back - stared death's mocking sentinel in the face and lived to tell the tale!!!

But they wouldn't have been impressed. No more than, I suppose, are you!"

During 1982 the Yorkshire Evening Post launched its wonderfully successful 'Half & Half' Appeal to raise funds equally for both Leeds Hospices, Wheatfields and St. Gemma's. These annual donations are always a memorable occasion and record the generous ongoing commitment of the citizens of the Leeds area. In just over a year the Appeal raised £140,000 to be split two ways and by 1990 the total raised to date was up to a staggering half a million pounds!

Wheatfields had cared for over 1,000 patients by the time it reached its fifth anniversary with over 60 employees, and it was inevitable that some of the 'founding fathers' would eventually retire. Arthur Tillotson had been Honorary Treasurer since taking retirement from the Bank in 1975, and we will never know how many hours or how much midnight oil had been spent over the years before he handed over a healthy reserve to his successor. In recognition of all his work he was appointed the first Honorary Vice President of Wheatfields. The new Honorary Treasurer, still active in his support for Wheatfields, was Malcolm Townsend M.A., formerly Research & Services Director with the Wool Industries Research Association.

The Honorary Administrator, Alex Bannerman, O.B.E., decided it was time for him to retire and hand over to a full time paid successor. Alex had given around 30 hours of voluntary service a week since he had retired from a career in the Probation Service. His wife, Myra, another dedicated volunteer, retired at the same time, after years of work with all sorts of duties, latterly as secretary of the Bereavement Group. Involved from the formation of the original Steering Committee as the Honorary Secretary, Miss Mary Stratton., M.B.E., B.A., finally retired after countless hours of service, including encouraging others to the cause. Hers was truly a lifetime of giving help to others.

Circa 1982.
Staff and volunteers pose for a group photograph on the main front lawn. To the left of the house was the Treasurer's office built in 1978 on the site of the old conservatory, now replaced by part of the Day Hospice.
(Collection Miss. L. Wood)

Five years on was a good time to take stock as plans for future development was always an important factor from the very outset at Wheatfields. The Hospice concept was, and still is, very much an innovative science and as such necessitates development by individual hospices to suit their requirements.

It had always been recognised that a Victorian house, albeit converted as well as possible, did not provide the ideal accommodation for patient care facilities. The intention always was to develop and thereby rectify any inadequacies when sufficient funds became available.

Much as the House Committee wanted to provide a day care centre, they had to wait years until the West Wing Coach House and Stable Block became available. Priority was given to reintroducing a bereavement service and the appointment of a nurse specialist (Mrs. Maggie Button) to visit patients and families at home prior to admission, as well as following up on patients who returned home.

This was the first step in providing a home care support service enabling the Hospice to extend its loving care to even more patients and their supportive families.

So it was decided that, as a first step, the current deficiencies in patient care facilities had to be remedied before additional services could be expanded.

To incorporate all the requirements a new single storey East Wing extension was designed by Architect John Fenton of the John Brunton Partnership. Patient accommodation was provided with 10 single bedrooms, a four bedded ward, plus sitting rooms and vastly improved bathroom and toilet facilities. The new extension, added to the two four-bedded rooms in the house, gave a capacity of 22 beds all on one level and released the upstairs rooms for much needed office space. The construction of this most attractive extension was entrusted to Messrs. M. Harrison & Co., who clad the external walls with dark reclaimed stone, allowing it to merge with the blackened facade of the Grade II listed house. The new wing was estimated to cost £370,000, another heavy burden for the already overstretched fundraising department which was now in the capable hands of Mrs. Rosalind Jenkins. Ros, as she preferred to be

The entrance hall in the early years of the Hospice with the new reception desk installed. The Italian marble mosaic floor is still as good as new.

called, came from a background of fundraising for Morley Rugby Club. She was one energetic lady who never took 'No' for an answer. She took on board the four popular annual events, Flag Day, Garden Party, Sponsored Walk and Christmas Fair, plus very active support groups and the very popular twice weekly sales of nearly new clothes in the 'big garage' at the Wood Lane end of the site, a useful relic of the wartime fire service days.

19th December 1984. Dr. Douglas MacAdam cuts the first turf to signal the start of the east wing extension in the presence of many supporters. To his right is Mary Stratton, next to her in the striped skirt is Barbara Barrett, central to the rear is Mary Murphy and to the left, hand in pocket is long service Honorary Treasurer Malcolm Townsend, and to his far left is Kathleen Merryweather.

Dr. Douglas MacAdam made a welcome return to England late in 1984 and during December he received the annual contribution from the Editor of the Yorkshire Evening Post Half & Half Appeal. On the 19th December in the presence of numerous friends and supporters he ceremonially cut the first turf to signal the start of the East Wing extension.

This was intended to be completed and handed over during the summer of 1986, but despite being on schedule, misfortune overtook the project at the 11th hour. A prolonged period of heavy rain caused a build-up of water, resulting in the high stone retaining wall at the corner of Grove Road and Alma Road collapsing. The reconstruction was another expensive undertaking but despite frustrating delays, on 25th October 1986, patients and staff moved into the new wing for the first time, a much improved working environment for the medical and nursing staff, which inevitably increased the quality of patient care.

Another setback came along at the end of a very successful garden party in July 1987, when part of the takings amounting to £950 was taken by raiders who threatened members of staff with pickaxe handles. Security of money has been a top priority at subsequent events.

When the 10th Anniversary of the Hospice came along in 1988, Chairman Murray Japp was serving a fourth year by special dispensation to mark him being the only remaining member of the first House Committee. In the Anniversary issue of the news sheet 'The Link', the Chairman wrote under the heading 'Our First Ten Years of Caring':

The roof trusses in position indicate the east wing extension is well on the way in 1985. (Collection Wheatfields)

"Even more important than the celebrations is the achievement of the ten years and the gratitude which we need to express to those in whose minds a hospice at Wheatfields was conceived and who worked so hard to make sure that its doors were opened. There is little doubt that they would have marvelled had they been able to look far enough ahead to see all that their vision and effort were going to achieve even as we now look back and see the great strides that have been made.

"I hope that in another ten years, those of us who are currently charged with the stewardship of Wheatfields will be able to look back and see advance and development of similar proportions. The conception, the continuation and the development of Wheatfields epitomise successive acts of faith, and the response to that faith, in so many ways, has been evidence that there are other than human hands at work. I believe those hands are the hands of God and that He will continue to bless and prosper our work if we allow our faith to blossom and grow. So, I have much confidence in the future prosperity of the work at Wheatfields. ...."

On Sunday, 30th October 1988, church bells over Leeds rang out peals of joy for two hours to herald in the 10th Anniversary of Thanksgiving in Leeds Town Hall at 3.30pm. This monument to civic pride was packed to the doors for a memorable and moving inter-denominational service where the address was given by the Right Reverend Malcolm Menin, Bishop of Knaresborough. No-one present could fail to be inspired when the voices of the combined choirs lustily sang 'Guide me O Thou Great Redeemer'.

CHAPTER 8
ON TO THE MILLENNIUM AND BEYOND

The Hospice had made great strides over the first decade of its development, but care in the community, like life itself, can never stand still. When striving to provide the best possible care there is no room for complacency, and with this in mind the House Committee under its new chairman, Jack Anderson, faced many weighty discussions of how to stretch the available resources. First priority was a much-needed expansion of the Home Care & Counselling services, with the provision of a Day Care Centre still high on the wanted list.

Inevitably a substantial increase in income was required, and fund raising took on a higher profile as the department expanded, and Ros Jenkins was promoted to the post of Fundraising and Publicity Manager. Much more forward planning was undertaken each year to maximise the returns on all the regular events, and to create new ones, along with more encouragement and appreciation for fundraising volunteers and individuals.

More sponsorship money started to come in as people organised marathons, walks, cycle rides and long distance Alpine Walks, parachuting, abseiling and swimming. One young lady even learned to swim, and then swam a mile to earn money for Wheatfields! Daring feats of bungee jumping took place, model railway shows were put on, some people slimmed, whilst others gave up drinking or smoking, all for charity sponsorship.

Probably the most successful individual fund raiser of the late 1980s would have to be George Linley, who braved all weathers collecting outside local supermarkets. Over his first two years his collecting boxes brought in nearly £6,000! Proud to display his running total on a placard, this 'bluff' Yorkshire character became almost a fixture at the Holt Park Shopping Centre, and over a six year period raised over £17,500.

Loyal support groups had from the early days generated wide publicity whilst raising considerable sums of money. At one time there were 24 very active teams of supporters who organised a continuous stream of fund raising events. Apart from the ever popular Coffee Mornings, these included all forms of sales, including outside shows, concerts, fashion shows, gardening, publishing recipe books, not forgetting the production of craft goods, knitwear and the mountains of home-made jams and chutney - the list is endless.

It is very difficult to highlight just a few of these wonderful teams, but mention must be made of the continued support of groups like:-Horsforth, Bramhope, Leeds 16, Wetherby, Otley, Gildersome, Derrick & Mary Taylor and the Dewsbury Baptist Church. The Tingley Group were very special, led by that most gentle of ladies, Margaret Nutter, who quietly,

George Linley, star collector for many years at local supermarkets, who over a six year period raised over £17,500.

each year, raised thousands of pounds for Wheatfields as well as finding time to be a regular volunteer in the Hospice at weekends until her untimely death in Wheatfields in February 1998. The Garforth Group were very active in the early years, organised by Gwen and Eric Bradley, who presented the Speakers Panel of volunteers with slide and video projectors as well as a handsome exhibition trailer donated in 1987, still in use to this day.

Ros Jenkins moved on to 'pastures new' in 1990, with the warm wishes of all at Wheatfields. Her appetite for tireless fundraising had certainly helped the development of the Hospice to progress. One of her many claims to fame was the introduction of another popular event.

'The Yorkshire Women of Achievement Awards' arranged in conjunction with the Yorkshire Evening Post, and presented at a luncheon in Leeds, has become a major event in the Yorkshire calendar.

In 1991 Rex Stacey, President of The Rotary Clubs of Leeds in its 75th anniversary year, chose Wheatfields as the charity to benefit from the celebrations, with two cheques during the year of £10,000 each.

The new Fundraising and Publicity Manager from March 1991 was Barbara Cresswell, who joined at another milestone when the annual running costs had doubled in the previous five years, and topped £1,000,000 for the first time. Barbara recorded in her first report to 'The Link' - "70% of that sum had to be raised by every way we can imagine"! Her words were to be rather prophetic as expansion of services were to be the order of the day.

The stable block freezer centre was soon available for purchase and development. Acknowledging that the treatment and care for people with cancer and other life threatening illnesses was developing into areas such as home based care and support, the stable block was purchased at a cost of £78,543 with the aim of creating a Day Hospice. Wheatfields also increased its number of home care nurses to match the increased demand. All was looking good for another big expansion when disaster struck on Trafalgar Day 1992. Yes, the 21st October was to be the day of the Great Flood!

At 2.00 p.m. a 30" water main burst outside the entrance to the big garage near the Wood Lane end of the site, and millions of gallons of water gushed out of a hole the size of a bomb crater, flooding the car park to a depth of 12" to 15". About 70 firemen were called in to try to avert a total disaster and makeshift temporary dams were erected across the car park to divert the torrent of water down Grove Road, where it raced down the slope at an estimated 20 mph. The front of the house was cut off for a time, and seepage necessitated the removal of patients from a four-bedded room. The worst damage, inevitably, was in the basement area, which had to be closed, leaving the lift out of order. The first estimate of the flood toll was at least £100,000, but in the best Wheatfield tradition, everyone rallied round. Offers of help poured in, and emergency food was provided by local shops. Some of the firemen said they had never been so well looked after, and Senior Divisional Officer Tony Rymer, on hearing we would have to cancel our Autumn Fair scheduled for two days hence, offered us the use of Moortown Fire Station for an alternative venue. The fundraising team gratefully accepted, and as it was this writer's responsibility to organise the revised event, it is nice to recall it went very well, and raised £2,500.

A volunteer's car - determined to get through whatever the weather!

It took several hours for the water to subside and reveal the enormous hole in the car park - approximately 12'0" in diameter by about 8'0" feet deep. One regular volunteer was horrified to find her car tied to a tree to save it from falling in the hole as it teetered on the edge of the chasm.

One other poignant memory of this time was Dorothy Fletcher's (nee Smith) who had worked at Wheatfields during the war as Secretary to the Chief Regional Fire Officer. Her husband, Bernard, was being cared for at the Hospice during the flood, and was one of the patients moved out of the water damaged four-bedded room. When Dorothy was shown into his new room memories flooded back, as she was amazed to find that his bed was in the same spot as her desk had been during the war! She still recalls, like so many other grateful people - 'I will never forget the wonderful care and treatment he received for almost a month.'

The annual 'Link' newsletter published just after the flood announced that the toll would be in excess of £100,000 and an Appeal was launched to help with possible cash flow problems. In his report, Chairman Jack Anderson summed it up well - "October 21st 1992 will be etched upon our memories as 'the day of the flood'. The unbelievable near-disaster was only matched by the unbelievable immediate and generous response of staff, volunteers and relatives of patients, and by the community at large during that evening and the following days. Thank you all for your swift and wonderful response." When the Appeal finally closed, the total raised was £22,735.

As the Hospice neared its 15th Anniversary it was about to enter a period of change and expansion. Dr. David Charley, the former Honorary Medical Director, and the last member of the original House Committee, decided to retire. Medical Director, Dr. Dawn Alison left to take up a senior post at the University of Leeds to be superseded by Dr. Kirsty Boyd, who was also working as Consultant in Palliative Medicine at Cookridge Hospital.

At the end of January, 1993, after 15 years of dedicated service as Matron and Hospice Manager, Miss Maire O'Donell left to take up a new challenge as a Counsellor and Trainer. In due course, on 1st March, Mrs Pat Riley was appointed as Hospice Director to take over the handling of an annual budget of £1.3m and the management of 90 members of staff.

Pat Riley had been Divisional Director for Social Services in Leeds, which made her the ideal candidate to review the agreement with Leeds Healthcare for more funding, as considerably more money was required to maintain the very high standards, and finance the proposed developments.

In keeping with the modern adage 'when the going gets tough, the tough get going' the One Million Pound 'Blackbird Appeal' was launched to provide a Day Hospice and in time, an Education Centre in the Grade II listed building, originally the coach house and stable block adjoining the house.

Many people asked 'why a Blackbird appeal?' This stemmed from patients in 1992 watching a blackbird make its nest in a garden bush where staff, patients and visitors watched its progress, and finally, everyone enjoyed seeing the three fledglings growing up and finally taking flight. The mother bird came back again, but sadly she flew away and did not return. Each year a keen watch is kept in case the garden attracts another would-be nest builder.

The civic launch of the appeal was held in the Henry Moore Lecture Theatre at Leeds Art Gallery on the 28th May 1993, when representatives of 125 companies attended and the Lord Mayor, Councillor Keith Loudon, officiated, and Martyn Lewis of the B.B.C. formally unveiled the plans of the conversion. Martyn, who is such an enthusiastic supporter of the Hospice movement, pointed out that 'helping Hospices is the most important thing that any community can do, and the work of the hospice movement is one of the biggest pieces of good news in Britain today. Every single day of every year 44 people die of cancer in Britain. But many live with it too - or live with another kind of life-threatening illness. It is absolutely vital that Wheatfields Hospice continues its journey along the Hospice path and continues to enhance its ability to deliver that care.'

The fundraisers, architect and builders certainly lived up to these stirring words, and eventually the finished building was completed to the highest standard possible, and is a testament to what can be achieved with the inside of an old building without, in essence, spoiling its very noble exterior.

Many volunteers took up the challenge to organise extra events to raise money. One arranged by the Fundraising Team was an evening show at the City Varieties by the well known local comedian Billy Pearce, who also invited along Joe Pasquale. It was an absolutely full house with people standing in places, and a never to be forgotten experience. Most who attended probably had never laughed as much in their lives. Funny it was, and yes, 'slightly risque' as well!

Mrs Nancy Hill took over as Chairman of the House Committee in the summer of 1993 to become Wheatfields first Lady Chairman, following a long association with the Hospice and a background of involvement with numerous other local charities. Around this time Michael Bourne, the volunteer responsible for the sorting and cataloguing of donated books for resale, announced his retirement. Since 1980, together with his team, he had raised over £85,000 from the sale of books, records and ephemera. He considered it was a good time to pack up the very heavy work of moving boxes of books in and out of the storage area. Happily, his retirement was a little like Frank Sinatra's final concerts which continued for years – Michael is still a regular volunteer, and is always going to retire next year!

Another stalwart volunteer, Simon Townson, that most enthusiastic of walkers who had been involved in all the annual walks, announced his partial retirement, due sadly to failing eyesight. Simon had been responsible for the creation of the 25 mile Dales Traverse which was added to the regular cycle of Wheatfield Sponsored Walks. The detailed description of the walk was published by 'Dalesman' in 1984, and since then Simon has sold badges and certificates to all who claimed to complete his challenge in under 12 hours.

Over the years the Annual Sponsored Walk in June has proved to be the most successful fundraising event. Since its inception in 1979 it has raised nearly half a million pounds. With a field of over 500 walkers some years, this can be a monumental task for volunteers on the day. Most of the 'key posts' have been filled by the same people each year. Brian Hicks acted as Walk Supervisor on 14 walks, and Derek Welsh and Paul Street were on the early walks, and are still involved with the very important task of organising the 'sweep team', which follow all the walkers to ensure no-one goes astray. Appreciation should also be accorded to the Raynet Organisation who provide radio cover over all the circuit – no easy job in some of the very hilly areas where radio contact can be a problem.

Slowly but surely the superb conversion of the coach house began to take shape, and in order to be well prepared to take over the new building a pilot Day Care service was introduced in June 1995 into the four-bedded room, which was the dining room of the old house.

The service was available for one day per week, with a second day being added in the November. Without doubt the best people to tell you about the Day Hospice are the patients, and typical of their recorded comments were:-

'Coming to the Day Hospice has given me an opportunity to share my worries and my fears. It has enabled me to unburden myself and talk openly about my illness, so that when I go home I am able to enjoy life without talking about cancer all the time.'

Members of the public are still surprised when told just how much of Wheatfields work consists of supporting patients and their families in their own homes. Yet the hospice annually looks after far more patients in the community than in-house.

Prior to April 1995 there were two separate teams of specialist palliative nurses working in the community in West Leeds – four based at the Hospice and three 'MacMillan' nurses at the Health Centre in Kirkstall. Good communication between these dedicated groups of specialist nurses was difficult to achieve. The Leeds Community & Mental Health Trust, which employed the MacMillan nurses, considered the service to patients would be enhanced if their staff became part of the multi-professional team at the Hospice.

In April 1995, therefore, the Wheatfields MacMillan Community Nursing Team came into being when three MacMillan nurses moved on to the Wheatfield site to join the resident team of four Home-Care nurses. With this integrated team of seven specialist nurses it was now possible to offer people facing life-threatening illnesses an even more effective and cohesive service.

John Taylor, House Committee Chairman, in the 19th Annual Review, recalled in Spring 1996 when Grey Construction Ltd. had completed the coach-house conversion (his first impression of the new extension) - 'We could hardly believe that the coach house could have been so completely transformed. The unsightly sixties windows, so out of keeping with the Grade II listed facade, had been replaced by leaded glass whose curves were echoed in the barrel vaulting of the ceilings, and every room glowed with natural light. At last we could plan a full day Hospice, staff training could be provided on site, and we could develop our specialist Hospice Library properly.'

We could scarcely contain our impatience to get into the building, equip it, and bring it into use!

The building was formally opened by the Lord Mayor of Leeds, Councillor Malcolm Bedford, on the 22nd October 1996, and was named, most appropriately, 'The Douglas MacAdam Wing.' Sadly Douglas was not able to be at the event, although he was represented by his sister.

The Day Hospice moved from its temporary base in the house to the ground floor of the Douglas MacAdam Wing in the same month - after 18 years Wheatfields was once again extending the care. In less than a year there was an increase of about 50% in the number of people being referred to this service, the majority of referrals coming from the Community Team of Nurses.

'Wheaty' found his own heaven on Earth after turning up on the Hospice doorstep as a stray kitten in 1996

The finishing touch to the superb frontage of the Douglas MacAdam Wing was to clear away the wilderness of weeds to create a new garden. After consultation with Day Hospice users, staff and volunteers, BHWB of Headingley produced many free designs before the one accepted did away with all formal lines in favour of rounded shapes and curves, with raised flowerbeds for wheelchair users, a pergola for climbing plants, along with a water feature and sitting areas. The final result completed over July and August 1997 is now a well-established garden, and an attractive addition to all the Hospice gardens, which reflects great credit on the Volunteer Gardeners' team who work every week – rain, hail or shine, led until 1997 by volunteer Head Gardener Don Mellor, who gave 16 years service.

The run up to Christmas each year is a busy time for the fundraising team, since 1995 led by Alyson Wort, and after two decades of continuous effort it is not easy to come up with fresh ideas. In Autumn 1996 it was the introduction of the first Wheatfields calendar – a quality product incorporating tear-off postcards, which proved to be a sell-out winner, and quite a sales job for Barbara Barrett, still a fundraiser after 17 years service. The following year the Christmas 'Lights of Love' were introduced, where everyone is invited to dedicate a light for, or in memory of, a loved one. Each dedication is recorded in a special book and a towering Christmas Tree festooned with over 1,000 lights illuminates the Hospice garden all over the Christmas period.

The first lighting of the tree is preceded by a short candle-lit service, a simple but uplifting and moving occasion, which ends with a most welcome glass of mulled wine and a mince pie.

In 1997, Pat Riley departed and was succeeded by the new manager, Jo Bewley, who brought with her considerable Hospice experience, having worked at St Catherine's in Scarborough and Dove House in Hull.

To provide the Hospice with more income that is regular and predictable, Wheatfields joined forces with St Gemma's Hospice in 1997 to introduce a joint lottery to benefit both Hospices, which has proved to be tremendously successful, thanks to the generosity and support of our thousands of members.

Warren Smith, a supporter of Wheatfields from the day it opened, and Chairman of the House Committee at the 20th anniversary of the Hospice, paid the usual tributes to all staff, volunteers and friends of Wheatfields, and went on to say after the Christmas Lights of Love service - 'There was a simple magic spirit of care and kindness felt on that

John Tuffen with physio Lynn Yeadon

occasion that will live with me for ever. That's the true nature of Wheatfields, which even a stranger cannot fail to notice. Despite much sadness there is a special kind of love and support which, dare I say, is unique.' Those optimistic words were well backed up later in the report with the annual statistics revealing the sheer volume of care provided for patients, and their families. The year recorded 295 admissions to the in-patient unit, 1,140 attendances in the Day Hospice and 1,485 visits by the Community Nurses. Great strides had surely been made in the first two decades of the development of Wheatfields.

The annual report for 1999 recorded a 20% increase in the number of patients admitted – 364 that year, plus a staggering 3,060 visits made by the Community Nurses.

With the ever increasing need for care for those suffering from life-threatening diseases and people with disabilities, the Sue Ryder Foundation, after nearly fifty years of service, decided that with the new Millennium approaching, a raised profile for the organisation was called for. 'Sue Ryder Care' was therefore launched in September 2000 and from that date the hospice in Leeds has been known as 'Sue Ryder Care Wheatfields.' Wheatfields has never stood still over its 24 years of service to the community. It has always been in a state of continuous development, and no change of title or logo can alter the total commitment to providing the best possible loving care to those in most need.

As we near the end of the story of Wheatfields to date, we cannot close without paying tribute to Lady Ryder of Warsaw, one of the greatest charity workers of the past century and described by the Yorkshire Evening Post as 'the true heroine of charity.' She died aged 77 on 2 November 2000 after a lengthy illness. Her first Home was opened in 1952 and she set up the Sue Ryder Foundation the following year. Now with over 17 Care Centres in Britain and several more in Eastern Europe, and around 500 Charity Shops, the new Sue Ryder Care has ambitious plans for future expansion, providing specialist palliative and neurological care throughout the UK, continuing to 'meet the unmet need.' Her name and spirit will therefore live on in the work of the charity she founded.

Looking to the future, it is true to say that maintaining an historic listed building can be rather like pebble dashing a dry wall - it calls for constant effort and expenditure to maintain and modernise its fabric and facilities without losing that special ambience of the 'Italian style villa.'

To end this part of the story, which after all is only a few chapters in a continuing saga, I think it very appropriate to quote Martyn Lewis, CBE, that champion of the Hospice movement, in his message to Wheatfields: 'I believe there is no cause finer than building and running Hospice services - helping week by week people whose own personal difficulty or disaster doesn't command any dramatic headlines.'

Notes

Notes

Notes

Notes